THE CURIOUS CASE OF CASE OF KARL NOVA

poems by Karl Nova
illustrations by Joseph Witchall
cover design by Greg Blackman

ISBN : 978-1-9997749-8-1

First published in 2021
by Caboodle Books

A Catalogue record for this book is available from the British Library.
Page Layout by Highlight Type Bureau Ltd, Leeds LS20 8LQ
Printed and bound by CPI Group (UK) Ltd, Croydon, CR0 4YY

The paper and board used in this book are natural recyclable products made
from wood grown in sustainable forests. The manufacturing processes
conform to the environmental regulations of the country of origin.

Caboodle Books Ltd.
Riversdale, 8 Rivock Avenue,
Steeton, BD20 6SA, UK.

Introduction

So here I am again writing the introduction to this second collection. I must first of all say thank you for taking the time to read this book of mine. This has truly been a labour of love.

When I wrote my debut book "Rhythm And Poetry" I only thought it would give me a few more opportunities to travel and carry on doing the hip hop flavoured workshops I had been doing up until that time. I had no idea it would take me to far off places like Cyprus, Turkey, China, Mongolia and across Europe to Luxembourg, Switzerland, Germany and Sweden. I didn't think it would win the CLiPPA poetry prize. I didn't even know about awards for books like mine. I had no idea I would become a Ruth Rendell Award winner for services to literacy. I am just a Hip Hop artist who saw the connections between rap lyrics, spoken word poetry and literature in general. I saw that young people were fully immersed and excited by the idea of reciting verses they could relate to. They saw it as cool already, so all I had to do was come in and show them how that is linked to literature in general. I wanted to show them that they have a voice and they could create with a cool bounce in their step. I just wanted to expand the idea of what poetry is and how rap was my door to that.

When it came to putting this collection together, at first I overthought it. I ended up getting in my own way. So I decided to go back to the basics and remember when no one knew me and I didn't have an awareness of any kind of external expectations. Honestly in the grand scheme of things I am just a drop in the ocean and that helped me get back on track. I just wrote as I was living and whatever part of my story resonated when I spoke in person, became the inspiration I would create verses from.

In this collection I gained more confidence and got bolder to share more. In my first book I didn't really do that although I sprinkled little personal stories here and there. The point before was to focus on the idea of poetry and how I got into that not my personal story. Now I think I am ready to share more because any time I have shared with people in person they would always go, "You should put that in a book you know" and I would respond with "Nah, I don't think so, maybe I will one day". So here we are. Coming from that angle, I can safely say this collection is a sequel to "Rhythm And Poetry". With this I am saying, I found rhythm and poetry and it enabled me to have the courage to share more of my story. Our memories, our journeys and our stories matter.

I don't really think of myself as a children's author, I know that is a weird thing to say. I don't approach writing in that way even though I know young people will read my books. I have approached writing these two collections with a mind to reflect on my own childhood and just honestly write as an adult reflecting. Working with young people doing workshops really helps me to do this because I learnt to really listen to them and talk to them on an eye level and never talk down to them.

I called this book "The curious case of Karl Nova" because honestly the more I reflect on how I got to this point of doing this, the more curious it appears to me. Maybe I secretly think I am Benjamin Button growing backwards like in the movie. I hope this collection encourages the idea that all our memories are precious and poetry can be a way to preserve and recall life's beautiful moments, paint pictures of those precious personal observations, immerse ourselves in the inner world of our imaginations and navigate the changing times that can be difficult and heart wrenching. Isn't that what poetry and literature in general has always done and so much more?

4

Contents

Wow You Actually Heard Me

I was thinking out loud
not really speaking to the crowd
I didn't think those outside knew
what I was all about
I thought this was just for a few
you know, people like you
Who would maybe be into
things I'm sharing from my view
I never knew it would connect
or cast such a wide net
and collect lots of attention
pulling people in
what's next?
now I feel I must reflect
and share more of my story

I must take this next step
no one else will take it for me
I'm sure we'll find common ground
to stand on once again
because we're all human deep down
that transcends every trend
but that fact won't erase details
that makes us different
uniqueness isn't a weakness
it is magnificent
it's to be celebrated
It is significant
I guess I'm just considering
that more ears are listening
to my heart speaking
I wasn't picturing
any of that at all
when I started scribbling

So here we are again, how do I start this? I think it would be a good idea to start here. This verse is a result of how my debut book went further than I could have ever imagined. You have to understand, when I wrote my first book "Rhythm And Poetry" in my mind, I thought it would just be a few people that would buy it. I thought only a few would "get" what I was saying. My hopes didn't go beyond having aspirations of getting more opportunities to do creative writing workshops as I had been doing.

I wasn't aware of the larger literary world at all. I wasn't aware of awards that a book like mine could win. It was a reflection on childhood and I really only had the young people I was working with in mind. I didn't think adults would care (apart from teachers and librarians). The reviews from young people mattered more to me than anyone else. I wanted them to know poetry was accessible to them in a relatable way that they could connect with. I didn't think anyone was paying attention to me in the wider world. I had good reason to think this way. I had been a Hip Hop artist and poet doing work in creative education for 8 years before my first book ever came out and the most attention I had gotten was being in a local Colchester paper twice! Even that came as a complete shock at the time.

Even though I write poetry to be heard, I was really surprised by those who ended up coming across my words. I don't make a big fuss about myself. I am quite a low key kind of person, which might seem strange since being a hip hop artist and performance poet means you have to get on a stage to perform.

I guess words written or spoken from your heart, have more power to strike a chord and resonate with people than I realised. In this collection I will share more of my story. I think I owe it to "younger me" because in "Rhythm And Poetry" I left out so many things I could have said. If I'm honest I left them out because I was a bit scared. I honestly didn't fully know what I was doing as an author, I was feeling my way through the fog and groping in the dark. That book was a torchlight for me.

Always remember, when you write or speak from deep inside, you really never know who is listening. You never know where what you say might end up but if you feel it inside, you have to find a way to speak. Writing has been my way to speak out those things I can't keep in.

So who do I write for now? First of all myself, and anyone with an ear to hear.

Before

Before I arrived the scene was set
before I drew a breath or could try to connect
the dots,
long before I could sketch
it seems the theme of my story was set
so picture this as I scribble this
I guess I wrote it all down to make sense of it
I had no say before but now I do so hear this
we're all affected by the choices of our nearest and dearest
I mean none of us chose to be born
and who would want to arrive and grow up feeling torn?
but I adjusted and adapted as well as I could
going through sharp switches from all that I knew
so sharp I think it
cut me in two
or into more pieces than that,
this is my truth
I put all the pieces back together
I spin yarns with humour
and have you in stitches forever

Life is amazing because it was already happening before you arrived. When we are born, we are arriving into a story that is already being told. Everything didn't start with you. Things had been going on long before you came here. My parents weren't married or together when I was old enough to understand things and ask questions, so finding out how they met took a very long time to discover. My parents are secretive people. I could talk about how they met in detail. I am not sure if I should. I might talk about that more later. Maybe I'm a bit secretive too.

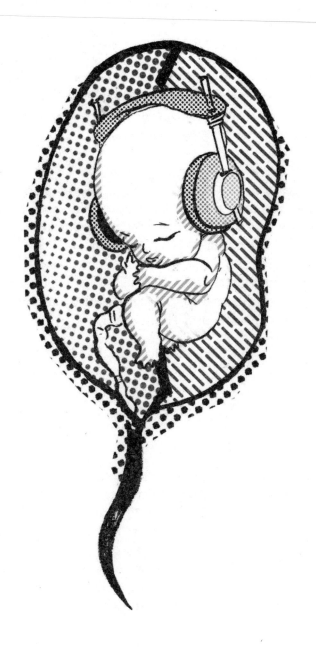

Asking how your parents met is a very interesting question. I think it is something everyone wants to know at some point. Isn't it intriguing to sit and think "I didn't ask to be born but here I am" I know I have thought about this a lot. I wish I could know who my great, great, great, great, great, great, great (insert more greats here) grandparents were. There are people who can trace their roots far back in that way. If I could do that it would be fascinating. I am a curious sort of person, I always have been.

If you have ever heard me speak in person, you'll know I crack a lot of jokes and have a wild sense of humour. I have people tell me that I should be a comedian. I don't know about that! I guess humour is like a spoon full of sugar that helps the sometimes bitter medicine of truth go down sweetly. I tell my story with joy and humour even though there has been pain and sadness. I don't want anyone to feel sorry for me because what I share is a story of overcoming. It is a story that is punctuated with laughter, joy and wonder. Well at least to me anyway. That is all that matters.

Earliest Memory

Somehow stored safely in the corner of my mind
is something so precious untouched by time
I dust it off sometimes like an old photograph
It's amazing what a young mind can grasp
I can remember my mum holding my hand
walking with me to the bathroom
please understand
I must've been about one, I was very young
but this memory has stuck with me for so long
she opened the door and put me in the bathtub
I felt like I was being cooked it was that hot!
I've always wondered why I can recall this incident
in my imagination it's so vivid, so intricate
even now when I close my eyes, I clearly see it
I often play it back but really do I need it?
nevertheless this is kept in my mind's treasury
So tell me what is YOUR earliest memory?

I have often heard people question if we can trust our memories. For example, you might recall something that happened before but someone else who was also present could correct some of the details or even have a totally different recollection of that particular incident. When this happens, you might begin to doubt yourself. Another thing is if you ask people what their earliest memory is, they might not be able to go back as far as this my first memory was able to go.

I am very sure this particular incident happened and can verify it from my mother because she was there. My age in this can be verified as well. I was actually a year old. We were living in North London in a place called Willesden. We lived in a single room in a house on Dean

Road. I didn't know those details until my mother told me this later when I was all grown up. I remember that room and I remember the bathroom was across a landing at the top of the stairs. I remember being put in a pail of water. Maybe it's the pain of feeling that hot water that seared this memory into my brain because it was steaming, piping hot!

My mother was very surprised I could recall this. I think our parents underestimate the power of our memories when we are little. Our brains are really like sponges soaking up everything. Maybe my memory is sharper than most, I can't say.

In this time we are in, we have all kinds of ways to record ourselves. I once saw a video on YouTube where a father recorded a video every day of his daughter from the day she was born until she was 20 and put it together in a sped up edited video. It's amazing. When I was a baby technology wasn't that advanced and even if it was with the way my life unfolded, I doubt there would be anyone who would even have the time to record me like that haha. I only have a few pictures from my childhood that can be found. I do have my memories though. All I have to do is close my eyes. What is YOUR earliest memory?

For My Blue-eyed Nan In Haverhill

I have no photograph of her
I just have flashes from my memory
I never forgot you
I wonder if you remembered me
you had a dog called Julie
that I loved truly
these memories running through me, deeply move me
you tried to teach me how to knit
and mend my socks
you took care of me when I had chicken pox
and the mumps and that time I bumped
my lip on the corner of the table, a big lump
I remember having, I still feel the scar
sorry for when I went missing and came back to cop cars
I was just a little boy enticed by my friends toys
I didn't mean to scare you with my choice
to go wandering off, at least I made it back
I didn't think dark woods were dangerous like that
I remember your grey hair, your blue eyes
and your big smile that was there all the time
we weren't related by blood but you were fam
you were my foster carer but I called you nan
I never thought my last goodbye was a permanent one
I thought I was going on holiday
I couldn't have been more wrong
but I was young
though I'm sure you got an explanation
that Lagos would become my home
not a vacation destination

Her name was Mrs V. Butterick. Until this day, I don't know what the V stands for. My earliest memories are filled with her. She lived in Haverhill in Suffolk. Her home was my home. I am pretty sure I was staying with her before I was 2 years old. The reason why I say this is because I remember my 2nd birthday being celebrated in her house with a party that my mother came to. She was old. I remember her saying to me she was in her 60s (maybe 70s). She was a lovely old English lady. As a child you hardly question things at first. It was all normal and the only reality I knew.

I wasn't the only one staying with her at first. I remember 2 other kids called Anna and Moses who were with me. They left when we moved to Hazel Close. At that point it was just Nan and I. That's what I called her. I have fond memories of her. I remember her smile, her laughter and things she would tell me and things she would do for fun like trying to tell the future by "reading" tea leaves in a tea cup. I think she did that for jokes to play pranks on me. Her family embraced me. I never felt unwelcome or odd. She really cared for me.

The way my life at the time went was, I stayed with her during school time and then holiday time I went to London to stay with my mother. So Easter holidays, summer holidays and Christmas holidays were spent in London and the rest of the time was in Haverhill. I even remembered the address she lived in from when I was a kid. First of all, she lived in a place called Lady Lane and then we moved to 21 Hazel Close in Haverhill. Both of these places are in Suffolk. No one told me this, these are things I recall straight from my memory as a kid.

Human Torch

I didn't think I was different
I was a child like everyone else
but one day my features and my skin
were ridiculed, pain is what I felt

I went home and told my nan
about the bullies that cursed me
she said "sticks and stones will break my bones
but words will never hurt me"

But she was wrong and for long
daily they would taunt me
and a fire inside me would build
as their words did haunt me

One day on the playground
by them I was surrounded
their words like sticks and stones
on my eardrums pounded

I couldn't take it anymore
the flames in me scorched
I erupted with anger
and became a human torch

I chased them down one by one
and gave them all a beating
I know I've talked about having no beef
but right then I was eating

In the head teachers office
I was treated like the problem
I knew then what I still know now
"I had to try to stop them"

Violence isn't the answer
but neither is blaming the victim
don't treat anyone as lesser
Just became they're different

The first school I remember attending was Burton End Primary school. Generally, I remember it was a pleasant experience apart from the time I got bullied. You see as a child, I didn't even think of myself as different in any way. It was only after getting bullied because of the colour of my skin and my facial features that I had any idea I was black. When I told Nan she tried to comfort me but I just didn't understand why being different was something that would make anyone want to harm me.

I remember in school, another girl and I were the only black people in the whole school and I noticed this only after I got bullied. She left the school after I had noticed she was there. I have often wondered what ever happened to her? Anyway, it was only me left and no one stood up for me so I stood up for myself and soundly beat them all. It probably wasn't the best solution but I didn't know what else to do.

Racism is ugly and senseless. Who taught those kids to use all those racial slurs and insults? We were only 7 years old! It must have been their parents or something they have seen older people around them do. If such evil and hurtful behaviour can be learnt so early, it must be unlearnt and treating people as equal and worthy of dignity must be learnt early as well. Having respect, compassion and treating people with proper respect and fairness must be learnt from day one!

No one taught me what to do, the instinct to fight back and defend myself came from inside me and it was what I felt I had to do. The taunts and bullying ended after that.

London To Lagos

Stepped out of the plane door
straight into heat unlike I had felt before
If this was a hug welcoming me it was uncomfortable
I was sweaty the temperature had me feeling combustible
took my mum's hand and walked down the stairs
I was 7 and a half and very glad she was near
Prior to flying out she told me, "hey!"
"we're going to Africa for a holiday, Okay?"
her words were a sticker that stuck to my brain
words I would revisit, again and again
in my mind they've stayed with me since
and over time these very words made me wince
The next day we took a taxi and rolled out
to a huge mansion I discovered was my father's house
Victoria Island, the neighbourhood was very nice
15 Idowu Martins street to be precise
she dropped me off like a delivery, there she left me
she said she'd be back the next day to get me
for only the 2nd time in my life I saw my dad
I wonder if when he first saw me he felt glad

I discovered I had two sisters and a brother
all younger and I met their mother
they all never knew I existed
and were never told about their distant sibling
The next day I waited for my mum to get me
I waited so long I wondered "did she forget me?"
As night fell my concerns rose
I was just a kid far away from home
A phone call came through and it was for me!

My mother's unmistakable voice is music when she speaks
I was told "be a good son to your father
and to the land you were born in you will return after"
at the time I never questioned it
I didn't even flinch
although over time her words made me wince
It was 2 whole years before I saw her again
It's tough having no choice or say about what's happening

2 years later, 9 and a half now
A phone call again my mother's lovely sound
I heard her voice telling me that she was in town
I felt such joy I was walking in happy clouds
I told my friends that I would be leaving
to head back to the city of my birth, I was beaming
She took me out for lunch and gave me lots of gifts
Only landing back in London could be better than this
The day was coming to an end I wondered when was our flight?
Was it gonna be in the dark? Because it was now night
My mother looked at me and said "it's time to go back home"
In my mind I was thinking "London and London alone"
My mother said, "be a good son to your father
and to the land you were born in you will return after"
She took me back to my father's house I fought back the tears
I didn't see her face again for 13 years!

It is amazing what the mind can remember. I remember this happened in May. It was the year of a World Cup. I can even remember the date of when I landed in Lagos, Nigeria for the first time ever. I had no idea it was going be the last time I would see the UK for a very long time. I didn't know it would be the last time I saw or spoke to Nan ever. It is only now as a grown up I realise that she knew. She probably couldn't tell me. I remember before going that I had to take a lot of vaccinations. I didn't understand why I had to take all these shots.

I remember we flew with KLM airlines. I really did think it was going to be a holiday. The previous year my Mother had taken me to Norway so I just thought it was going to be a trip like that. I don't think anything prepared me for this.

When I have told people about this, they have wondered why my mother chose to take this kind of action. They're like "How could she do this?" Mothers especially are like, "wow". Well, I wondered for my whole time in Nigeria. I had to wait years and years for answers, so you are going to have to wait and be patient. All will be revealed. I think that is how life is sometimes. Some things don't make sense until they are past tense. As the Danish philosopher, poet and author Søren Kierkegaard says "Life can only be understood backwards, but it must be lived forwards"

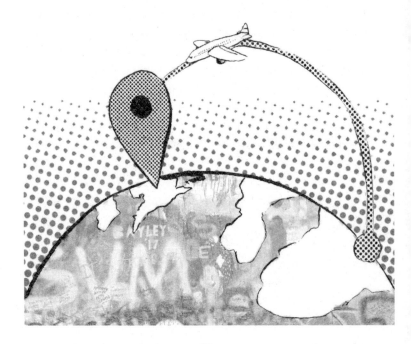

How Could You Leave Me Here?

I thought I was just spending the night
I thought that much was clear
but you're not coming back to get me, why?
How could you leave me here?

I waited all day
and sat by the door with no fear
I trusted you when you said you'll come
How could you leave me here?

Will I ever see you again?
Will you ever be near?
What's going to happen now?
How could you leave me here?

I have no choice in this do I?
I wish I could disappear
I might as well be invisible anyway
How come you leave me here?

So there I was in my father's house, far away from everything I had ever known. I really did think my mother was going to come and get me. At the time if I am being honest, I just accepted it once I found out that wasn't going to be the case. It was only the next day when my stepmother, probably after finding out I was here to stay, shouted at me that I cried. She said to me "You better go back to where you came from!" In my 7 and a half year old mind I thought "If only I knew how!" and I cried that day. I cried so much I remember saying to myself "I must never cry like this again" My stepmother ended up leaving a year after I arrived but that's another story.

I had eaten boiled yam and red tomato stew for the first time and didn't like it. I had thrown it all up and found it hard to sleep. This was it, my new home and I had no say in the matter. I had to trust that somehow this would make sense and things would get better, one day.

LIT

Power cuts were a normal thing
You got used to the darkness
It was fun to have candles lit
to push back some of its harshness

The next thing you heard was a whir
The generator starts to hum
The whole street is a cat that purrs
houses are lit one by one

Candles blown out wishes granted
Over my head lightbulbs glow
An idea has been planted
In my mind that seed grows

for a dark place to be lit
a power source is needed
What ignited me was a gift
It came to me as I was seated

I was sitting in a dark place
I felt abandoned all alone
but this gift lit up my face
and it was mine to own

books in my hand became magic doors
opening up to universes
my mind lit up and my heart soared
and darkness cannot reverse it

The culture shock I went through while adjusting to life in Lagos after only knowing life in the UK was a lot to deal with. One of the things that became strangely normal were the power cuts that happened frequently. You could be watching TV and be right in the middle of your favourite tv show and the electricity would cut off just like that! Luckily for me my dad had an alternative power supply.

The huge compound as we called it, or estate we lived in that was owned by my dad had a huge power generator. Once NEPA (National Electric Power Authority which Nigerians jokingly called Never Expect Power Always) which is now known as PHCN (Power Holding Company) cut the electricity supply, my dad would have one of the people that worked for him switch it on and we would have the

power back on. Not everyone in Lagos had that kind of privilege. Sometimes power could be out for days!

It became so normal for power to be cut off. It became a joke to us kids. We would shout "NEPA!" when it happened and laugh our heads off! "Never expect power always" we would shout while we waited for the generator to be switched on. Sometimes it would take a while for the generator to be switched on and we would have to light candles. Also, you would become more aware of mosquitoes. Don't get me started about mosquitoes! They would fly close to your ears and you could hear a whining kind of sound and when you tried to kill them you would more times than not, end up slapping your head or slapping whatever part of your body you felt they had landed on. Mosquitoes can give you malaria fever and I can't even tell you how many times I got that! It didn't even occur to me as a child how deadly it is because the cure for it was freely available and you would be fine after a couple of days of high temperatures, headaches and feeling awful.

It is no wonder in my verses I talk about light a lot. Originally, I wanted to call this book "LIT" as a play on words. Lit has multiple meanings. Lit, because we all love when lights have a place lit up. Lit, because that is short for literature and lit because that is just slang these days to say something is cool. Yep that's LIT!

What If Books Could Read?

What if a book could read you?
flip the pages of your heart with all your thoughts fully viewed
not judge you by your cover
how you look externally
but could peer inside your mind
understanding you internally
even if you're not verbally speaking out all the time
Imagine if there was a book that could read your mind?
hanging on your every word, your sentences and chapters
amused by all the plot twists, sadness and laughter
not just skimming through but reading you intently
not throwing you around but treating you gently
never leaving you half-read or tossed aside
but finding you interesting enough to go on the ride
of really finding out what's on your inside
paying attention to all the details of your life
what kind of book would you be?
and how would you want the pages of your life to read?

When I travelled from London to Lagos with my mother, I didn't know she had packed books into my bag. The book I remember reading at the time was "The Lion, The Witch and The Wardrobe" which is from the classic "Chronicles of Narnia" series that I loved. That whole series and that book especially has always been one of my favourites. I have probably said this many times already elsewhere. In a strange way I think books were how I felt connected to her because she always bought me books. In fact while I was in Lagos, she would post books to me or send someone from London with a package for me that contained things like clothes, magazines, video games, toys and books.

29

Have you ever read a book that was so good you feel like you are inside the book? It is amazing when that happens. I was once reading an adventure book and was so engrossed that I felt my heart beating faster. The room I was in disappeared and I had to drop the book because it became TOO REAL.

Sometimes a book feels like it is reading you and revealing all your secret thoughts. It feels like it is speaking straight to you. This is something all authors truly aspire to achieve. I have been told these parts of my book where I share this way feels like that by some very nice people. It makes sense for this kind of personal meeting of hearts and minds to happen when you write from the heart and read with understanding and full attention.

I'm thankful reading was a way of escape for me. I am thankful for authors who take the time to build worlds with their words so that our imagination has a place to go because life can be harsh and unkind a lot of times.

Look And Go On Slowly

There are times time seems to decide to
start slowing
and sitting here feels like I'm not going
anywhere
If you have air conditioning blowing cool air
be thankful because the truth here
could be you're going to be in this
for a long time
it feels like this heat could melt you
though it can't unfreeze time
it's hard to describe being in this
even harder to imagine going through this
every day I miss
the London version, it's nowhere near this severe
Oh! We just moved a few inches,
it feels like a whole year
since we moved before
they say the inch makes the mile
over here this is called "go slow"
the thought of that makes me smile
people tap on windows trying to sell you things
anything from newspapers, sausage rolls,
cold water, soft drinks
sunglasses, necklaces, slippers, cuff links
wallets, peanuts, bread, rings and earrings
shoes, clothes, watches, televisions!
the industry of street traders is quite a mission
frustrated drivers continuously beeping car horns
it sounds like the vehicles are arguing I wish I was warned
because nothing can prepare you
maybe with time I'll feel cosy
but for now I just
look and go on slowly

In Lagos it is called "go slow" I am talking about a traffic jam. You haven't experienced a traffic jam until you have been in a Lagos one. It is quite an experience. Traffic jams in London are a walk in the park compared to them! You had better be in a vehicle that has full air-conditioning because you might be there for a while and the heat can be almost unbearable. You also need to have a good stereo system to keep you entertained.

One of the first things I learnt while in Lagos was that someone had turned the word Lagos into an acronym for Look And Go On Slowly. It was something people said as a joke when talking about life in Lagos. What it meant in conversations normally was that if you see something happening on the streets, mind your business and move on but since people are curious, you can move slowly in order to find out as much as possible hahahaha!

When moving through traffic jams in Lagos, it is guaranteed that there will be street traders or hawkers as they are called trying to sell you something and believe me you could buy anything! All the things I named in the poem and more are things you can actually buy while sitting in your car!

While in traffic jams in Lagos be careful though, I have heard stories of people who had their windows down getting anything from watches, phones and laptops stolen by thieves who'll freely take things off you right out the window.

The First Embrace

The first time I heard the drums and the bass
from the speakers
the sound hit me and pulled me in deeper and deeper
In my heart something was tugging me
I felt the warmth of the melody hugging me
whispering in my ears, "I'm here my dear"
I felt safe in this embrace, what is this I hear?
It's like I'm starting from scratch am I being reborn?
transformed by what I'm hearing performed
My heart feels like it's in sync with the rhythm
It's like I found a part of me inside this sound system
I didn't work for it
but I've been paid in full
by the richness of the sound
verses embedded with jewels
my head is spinning with the spinning of tunes
I could feel it in my chest as the sound filled the room
I got the message loud and clearly that day
rhythm and poetry found me
and stayed

If you have ever seen me in person, you probably have heard me talk about my older cousin. Well this verse is about the moment I heard hip hop for the first time because I happened to be around when he was playing it. It was a major turning point for me. The first songs I heard were "Paid in full" by Rakim and "The Message" by Grandmaster Flash and The Furious Five. I found out later that these were classic hip hop songs.

Not only did he play all this music, he taught me about Hip Hop culture and it really did feel like school but a different kind of school. I am grateful for his guidance because I was only a kid but he was knowledgeable and more experienced. It was all fascinating. I felt like the music was embracing me. At that time, I needed an escape. Reading, music and video games were my first favourite things that caused me to tap into my imagination.

When I was a kid I couldn't afford to buy music for myself so I had to rely on his collection and listening to his stereo player. One day he did something so amazing for me. He actually gave me his stereo. It was a portable one that had powerful speakers. I would record songs from the radio on cassette tapes and make my own mixtapes full of my favourite songs.

Apart from him doing that for me, we would write raps together and it was all this that got me into writing my own rap verses and poems. My cousin had to leave and go to Holland. He is a University professor right now in Ireland. He really challenged my thinking and always pushed me towards thinking for myself and developing a thirst for knowledge. One of the principles of hip hop is holding knowledge in high esteem. Many people look at commercial rap music today and sadly probably can't see this core value anymore. Thankfully I had my cousin to teach me all about that. This is why the content of my music today leans into sharing knowledge. I want to uplift, inform and inspire just like my cousin did for me.

Rooftop Boy

This really happened I want to tell you the truth
I had a great idea
"why don't I climb up on the roof?"
I was just a little kid but this is what I did
there was a house a little smaller
in the estate I lived
I had thrown something on that roof
and had to get it back
I think it was a tooth that fell out
in some tissue it was wrapped
I was told that it had to go under my pillow
for the tooth fairy to take it or a new tooth wouldn't grow
somehow I climbed up and there I was
feeling excited I can't lie I felt a buzz
I also felt like Spider-Man up there I was crawling
I had no fear of heights or even falling
suddenly I heard a loud voice booming my name
I froze it was my dad his words burnt like a flame

"Karl what are you doing? Come down right now!
See me in my room in 15 minutes!!" I was like wow
My heart sank as I climbed down
I was in deep trouble but I wasn't gonna drown
I went to my room and started to count down
the minutes on the clock I had to figure out
a plan
I had a lightbulb moment,
I knew what I would do
I tucked some clothes into my shorts
made sure it looked smooth

It was time so I headed to his room
knocked on his door
my heart pounding
time to meet my doom
"Come in!" His voice boomed
I went in and there he stood
with a clothes hanger twisted that I knew he would
use on me but I was prepared though scared
I shivered as he gave me a cold stare
I got spanked with the twisted hanger turned into a cane
but I was padded up so I felt no pain
I acted hurt I screamed and acted wild
He shouted "go to your room!!"
I turned and left with a smile

It was called the "boys quarters" It was a bungalow style building with many rooms and it was part of the huge compound or estate that my father owned. It is where people who worked for him lived. My dad had a driver, cook, gardener and at some point even a guy who washed his clothes. In the huge estate my grandmother lived next door as well as a beloved uncle of mine and two aunts. Another uncle lived in another house at the back where there were extra apartments that were rented out to tenants.

It was the roof of the "boys quarters" that I climbed and got caught by my dad. I didn't think it was dangerous. I just wanted to get my tooth back. I used to climb trees, fences and just about anything I could as a kid.

Corporal punishment was normal when I was growing up in Lagos. It hurt when you got beaten and hurt even more when you felt you were unfairly beaten. That was life though, you just made sure you didn't get caught doing something naughty like climbing the roof of the boys quarters where your dad could clearly see you from his bedroom window. You might think you are spider-man but you are definitely not the invisible man or in my case, "invisible boy".

Physics Prison Break

To speak of this now
might sound so out of place
like a time traveller from another time
but I know some can relate
I must tell this tale
it was a normal thing
I wonder how it will sound
will it make your ears ring?
I was in the physics lab
to have a boring physics class
when I decided with my friend
to sneak out quick and fast
we got out of the door
and crept down the stairs
we both felt so sure
we had escaped but weren't aware
of the physics teacher watching us
with a cold stare
on the balcony he stood
his loud voice made us scared
"WHERE ARE YOU GOING?"
his voice boomed and made us freeze
my heart sank like the titanic hitting that iceberg
my knees, went weak
"BOTH OF YOU COME BACK UP HERE!"
back up the stairs we went
everyone was silent the whole place felt so tense
the teacher stood
with a long cane in his hands
he pointed to a table
and said "one of you lie flat"

My friend stepped forward
and got on the table
he took 6 lashes
I wondered how he was able
to take everything
without hardly flinching
I thought "it can't be that bad"
though I was already wincing
It was my turn
I braced myself
the first strike
burned my back up
but I didn't cry
by the time he got to three
it was too much for me
I hopped off the table
and started begging for mercy
the teacher said
"HOW DARE YOU, I AM STARTING AGAIN FROM ONE
IF YOU JUMP OFF AGAIN THE SAME THING WILL BE DONE!"
my eyes were stinging, ears ringing, back blazing
I got back on the table and held tight, emotions raging
I took everything the pain was too much
I stayed put only because I clutched
with a tight grip and in my mind I asked myself
"why did we try to escape from this physics cell?"

Schooling in Nigeria is different from how it is in the UK. That right there is an understatement. Whenever I tell people especially students, how corporal punishment was a thing they are shocked. I can't say if teachers are still allowed to beat students right now though. (I am willing to say it still happens today, don't quote me though).

I was a good student. Always in the top 3 of my class in primary school and I got one of the best academic results but I was a bit naughty sometimes and I've been beaten with canes, wires, blocks of wood (yes you are reading right!) and rulers.

Secondary school was a whole other world and even stricter. I went to a boys' secondary school, St Gregory's College and it was not easy. Every day felt like anything could happen.

I don't know why my friend and I thought it was a good idea to try to sneak out from the physics lab but we did it and got caught. Everything in that verse was a true story.

Corporal punishment was once a thing that happened in British schools. To put it simply, if you were naughty your teacher could beat you! Nigeria being an ex-colony of Britain kept the old system of British education down to corporal punishment. I can't even imagine how it was when physical punishment was allowed in British schools. It was so normal for us in Nigeria that I don't even think we could imagine any other way of life at that time. I know some people reading this are probably thinking how mad it is that to us it was the norm.

There was a guy who was a senior that retaliated and actually slammed the vice-principal of the school on the floor. He had been told off for breaking one of the many rules and even been hit by the VP. The news of him slamming him to the ground spread through the school and we were all amazed.

An emergency assembly was called and he got beaten in front of the whole school by all the teachers who were known to be brutal with canes. He didn't even flinch after more than 60 lashes and until this day is spoken of as a hero amongst ex-students hahaha

Learning To Take An L

It's not easy taking an L
we do not take them well
no one likes to fail
we all cried when we fell
as little children taking our first steps
no one was born walking
after taking their first breath
I walked in a huge shadow of success
so when I fell into a pit of failure
it felt like death
I had to repeat a whole year
I fell far behind
I felt so much shame
tears almost drowned my eyes
a dark cloud became my companion
day and night
harsh words from my Dad
ripped my heart and mind
I was such a disappointment in his eyes
He looked at me and I didn't reflect
the success of his time
depression became a blanket
I would sleep with at night
a dark cloud of sadness stole away my smile
but I'm sure you've heard about
clouds and silver linings
I fought back the blues
with the jewels I found while writing

When I got to the SS2 which in the UK is the equivalent of being in Year 11, something bizarre happened. It started with a mix up from my teacher who had written in my report card that I had passed Maths and then said he had written the wrong result in and that I had failed.

My Dad even came to school to meet the teacher to talk about it. He refused to accept he was wrong and this meant I had to repeat the whole year. That is how the system was. For someone like me that had always been a top student, this was devastating. My Dad was so upset that he said some very harsh things to me that I can't even repeat. I cried and cried. My Dad had been a top student all his life so for his first son to fail this way was a disgrace.

That summer holiday felt longer and lower than any I had ever had. I know I have mentioned this somewhere before, but it was my younger sister Marie that suggested I just write all my feelings out to get through. She knew I loved writing and her suggestion was the right thing to do. I think at the time I took writing even more seriously. It was a way out of a dark place.

I had to go back to school and repeat that year while my friends moved up to the next class which was the final year of Secondary School. I had some friends who had to repeat as well. It was the worst feeling ever. It was the longest year ever for me at the time. I had no choice.

I got through and it is all history now. Sometimes in life you have to learn to take an L. That just means you have to learn to take a loss. When you learn to take an L, it becomes a lesson and a blessing in a very good disguise.

Life Is Not A Video Game

Life is not a video game
but imagine if it was
and you had to trust a gamer
with control pad plugged
into a console
I hope whoever that was had a cheat code
so I could have extra life
and finish levels on beast mode
up, up, down, down, left, right, left, right,
be a winner every day
Push the buttons stay sharp
you better master the game
I could be a skilled fighter
advancing to higher levels
My mind could craft a whole new world
or push the pedal
and rev my engine in any race car I want
and do all kinds of stunts or be on a battlefront
or switch things around
and play at the World Cup
raise the difficulty level go on turn it up
score the points, feel the rush
advance the story beat odds and ops
dodge the cops, get your energy topped
It's just a game
but it feels like there's more to it
Life is not a video game
hold on maybe it is

These days I am not much of a gamer. When I was a kid growing up though? I was into video games heavily. My favourite games are Streetfighter IV (or any of the versions after that) and FIFA but I think Streetfighter edges it as my favourite game ever. I'm still good at it and have the app on my iPhone!

I remember when I was in secondary school, a couple of arcades were opened in Victoria Island. I remember there was Entertainment World and Mad House. My friends and I would go there ALL the time. We would spend all our money there.

One day, and I say this with shame, myself and a couple of my friends, escaped from school by jumping over the school fence. We did this just so that we could go to Entertainment World or E World as we called it. I packed extra clothes in my school bag and changed in their toilets when I got there. I never got caught but I only did it once. There were so many of us in a class and the teachers weren't always there so no one noticed we were gone!

It's so mad that I did this because I actually had a video game console at home as well as a portable Gameboy. I guess it was the rush of escaping school that made me do it. The same kind of rush when you're playing your favourite game and escaping the bad guys. I guess life was like a video game for us because as we jumped over the fence, the security guard at the front gate chased us for a little bit through the streets. We got away. Mission accomplished. Game over.

Not All Heroes Are In Comics

Not all heroes are in comics
Not all heroes wear capes
Not all heroes are bionic
Not all heroes have superpowers okay?

Not all heroes have a cool origin story
Not all heroes have their own theme song
Not all heroes have fame and glory
Not all heroes escape going unsung

Not all heroes have a secret base
Not all heroes have a sidekick
Not all heroes have their own video game
Not all heroes are cool and slick

Not all heroes go viral on social media
Not all heroes get a news feature
Not all heroes have a page on Wikipedia
Some of those heroes are my teachers

At some point I got into collecting comic books. I was very much into Spider-man especially, he was my favourite. I was into Marvel and DC Comics though I leaned more towards Marvel. DC had Superman and Batman though and those are classic characters. I wish I knew more about Black Panther back then. I knew of the Black Panther comics but never collected them, I only really knew more about that character because of the amazing Marvel movie that was released in 2018. It remains my favourite movie from the Marvel cinematic universe.

I used to exchange comics with my friends. Sometimes I wonder how I had time to play video games, read books, watch tv shows and movies, play football, read comics and still do all my school homework. Maybe I had superpowers. Well, not really.

We loved superheroes because we wanted to be them and have their powers. We saw ourselves in their sometimes quirky stories as well. During my time in Nigeria there were Nigerian comic heroes too. The one I remember the most was a daily comic in the Vanguard newspaper called Mojo.

I have already spoken of my schoolteacher in the introduction of "Rhythm And Poetry" so all I will say here is, good teachers are heroes. You can actually substitute the word teacher in the final verse with all the everyday unsung heroes you can think of. I could give you some more examples like our public healthcare workers and carers. I'm sure you can think of more. Our real-life everyday heroes walk amongst us. Let's celebrate them.

Homecoming?

On the land of my forefathers
I've been ten toes down
Oh wow! I wrote down my thoughts
to slow down
this moment
so how did I feel?
my mind was roaming
like the door to my village
I kept it open
my features told stories
that elders translated
though they mostly spoke with
my native tongue so ancient
up until then I was a London boy planted
in Lagos soil
I didn't fully understand it
my father never spoke to me in our language
any knowledge I had is because I snatched it
so there I was feeling like a foreigner at home
feeling very embarrassed so I hardly spoke
"I see my dad in a different light" is what I wrote
in a journal that I kept hidden underneath my clothes
A strange discovery I made that shook my dome
I looked around the compound and saw tombstones!

Even though my father, a couple of my uncles, my aunts and my grandmother lived in Lagos, my family's roots are in the east of Nigeria. My family is from Owerri in Imo State. We are Igbo people.

Where we lived in Lagos is part of the land of Yoruba people. The common language of Nigeria is English due to us being an ex British

Colony that had gained independence. You have to understand in Nigeria there are over 525 languages! There are 3 groups of people that are the largest which are Yoruba, Igbo and Hausa people, so English is what we all speak and that holds the country together. There's also a broken English or as we called it pidgin English that is predominantly spoken. I can still speak it now and if I ever used it in London, it would sound like a foreign language if you've never learnt it though you might be able to catch the English words in it.

My dad never spoke Igbo to me and I couldn't speak Igbo as a child. I could understand it to a degree because of hearing the people who worked for my dad speak it. I also remembered some words my mother would speak on the phone to her friends and relatives when I was in London before she brought me to live in Lagos.

Going to visit my village in East Nigeria with my dad was a big deal. The name of my village is Ezeogba which is in Emekuku, an area in the city of Owerri. I felt like an outsider because I couldn't speak my native tongue but I also felt I belonged at the same time. They could tell I was very British, I mean my accent was still so British even though I had been in Lagos for some years by this time. It was a fascinating experience. The elders could look at my face and know who I belonged to without me saying a word. I don't know what I expected when I got there.

I'm not sure if I expected to see little huts but the village is very modern with houses like any other town I had been to. When I was in the UK, I think the idea in my mind was it would be full of huts and kind of primitive. It was far from that. It is very beautiful and peaceful there. This might sound wild but there were no mosquitoes there. I slept with my windows open and didn't get mosquito bites unlike in Lagos, where I would have suffered a lot of bites if I left my windows open like that.

The discovery I made about tombstones being around the village is true. Igbo people believe that death isn't to be feared and it is all just a cycle. You're born, you live, you die and then someone else is born and it keeps going. Burying loved ones underneath living rooms and in front porches was normal. It wasn't done all the time but it happened. I know it sounds spooky and honestly it freaked me out when I noticed at first but after a while it was normal and it didn't spook me anymore.

First Son

He was his Dad's first son
and I'm his first son too
not first child although at first
I had no clue
but being a boy seemed to
carry more weight
It's what I was told
a point I was forced to take
A huge shadow cast by
Grandpa late and great
He departed before I arrived
on life's stage
but I've walked on streets
after him named
I've questioned if his blood
flows in my veins
My dad offered me a path to walk
that was paved
with promises of greatness
but it wasn't mine to take
so I broke tradition
dropped it and broke away
I had to follow my heart
my art led to the stage
to the naked eye
it seems like we parted ways
but we're forever connected
by words on a page
because writing you see
was part of his dream
reminding me of the apple
not falling far from the tree

I have struggled with the idea of using actual names while telling parts of my story but I decided against it. My grandfather on my father's side was a great man. He was the first Minister of Commerce & Industry as well as transport & aviation in the first republic of Nigeria. I'm sure if you did some digging you would find out who he was. When Nigeria became independent, he was one of the people in government that was there who endorsed and backed that historic move. He has addressed the British government in London during a crucial time which was the Nigerian civil war in the 60s calling for the ceasefire to that. I never got to meet him because he passed on before I was born. I did meet my grandmother who showed me a picture of them shaking hands with the Queen.

My father is his first son and in Nigerian cultures, being the first son carries the weight of certain privileges like for example being the main heir to any inheritance. My dad tried to walk in his father's footsteps. He went to Harvard University and graduated with honours, he went to Kings College London as well and the London School of Economics and graduated with honours from there too. He became a National Planning Commissioner and was an economic adviser during President Olusegun Obasanjo's democratic presidency.

I found out when I was 10/11 that my dad had another child that the rest of us four children didn't know about. She is older than me by exactly a year and 3 days. She lived in the USA and she came to visit with her mother. I took to her immediately and we have remained close ever since. Even though she was born before me, simply because I was born a male child, I get to have certain privileges that she doesn't. That is how the culture is. I guess it is because the male children carry on the family name. Tradition is a strange thing.

I am my father's first son and I have no interest in being involved in politics. I have even less interest when it comes to Nigerian politics which can be dangerous and corrupt. It is just not in me to be involved and I know my father has not been happy with this. He told me that if I really wanted it, I could be a senator, then governor and maybe even run for President. I don't care about all that, my heart had been captured by the arts. I knew I wanted to be a writer from the moment I fell in love with words through hip hop and spoken word poetry.

The ironic thing about all this is I found out later on that my dad's real dream was to be a writer. He had written 2 books before I was even born but his father told him to study law and he ended up being in government. I remember my dad used to be on TV a lot in Nigeria talking about things like the budget. As a child those things were boring to me but it was amazing to see him on TV! He even had his own column in one of the top newspapers in Nigeria for a long time. My dad has retired from government and is back writing books. He has written one which is published and is writing another.

Isn't it funny that I am writing books and so is he? I guess the apple doesn't fall far from the tree. We aren't close today but that is another story for another time.

All Of Us Were Ballers

I had seen a few London summers but never felt heat like this
It felt like the Lagos sun was giving me a kiss
with flaming lips on my cheeks my face was burning
Sweat poured down my face my feet were hurting
I was playing football on the street with nothing on my feet
going hard at it on the concrete where daily we would meet
Makeshift goalposts made of shoes, stones or clothes
is what we used they were called monkey posts
We would play matches for hours on the road
not on high streets but side streets or a close
And not once do I remember getting sun stroke
though I do recall blisters on my feet and hurt toes
No referee, no yellow or red cards
We played hard and today I still have some scars
most of us would never be professionals but so what?
every time we played we felt like we were at the World Cup

As a kid in Nigeria, football was everything. When I was a child, I didn't understand all the issues the country was facing. There were riots sometimes and worker strikes. I remember when there were teacher strikes and we had to stay at home for a long time. I might not have understood everything going on but one thing I totally knew was when there was a football match with Nigeria playing, the whole nation would stop to watch.

When Nigeria won the gold medal at the Olympics in Atlanta, it was the most amazing time. I ran out on the streets to celebrate. It was crazy. It is a time I will never forget ever. We even beat Brazil and Argentina to achieve this amazing feat. It made all of us want to be footballers.

We played football everywhere and anywhere. I used to play football barefoot on the streets all day long in the hot sun. I was the child of a rich man and wasn't supposed to be playing street football but I didn't care. When we played football, it didn't matter what your background was. All that mattered were your skills and the heart you showed on the "pitch". Our pitch was the hot road and we went hard at it. All of us would run around imagining ourselves to be Kanu, Okocha or any of Nigeria's football heroes. All my friends were ballers!

Barbershop Talk

Welcome to the barbershop
oh you thought it was just to get a haircut?
have a chair
wait your turn
stay alert
you will learn
that this is like a country club
or being on a movie set
act one, scene one
the lines delivered here connect
When it's your time in the chair
you'll feel like it's a throne
you'll feel like the world is owned
by you, it sets the tone
for your whole day
your whole week
trust me
you'll feel fresh
like the sweet ocean breeze
you'll see
there's always someone
sharing wild stories
or others having a loud debate
like they're performing
for everyone watching and waiting
to get shaped up
clippers whir, music blasts from a speaker
razors
are sometimes used for finishing touches
talc powder is applied with small brushes
last of all you get sprayed up it stings a little

now step out of the chair, it is official
you're ready to face the world
You'll feel sharpened
now display your work of art
great barbers are artists

When I was a kid, I wasn't fond of getting my haircut. I remember once a barber was brought to our house to cut my hair. He ended up giving me a hairstyle I didn't even like! I was so upset I cried! It only happened once because normally I went to the barbershop myself where my favourite barber knew how to hook me up with a proper shape up.

A man's relationship with his barber is a very important one. He's the guy who knows your hair and how you like it done. When you have a good relationship with a true professional, it's the best thing to pay him a visit. It's almost like going to see a family member after a while.

The barbershop is truly a whole thing you have to experience. The conversations you get to hear, the stories that are shared, the debates that are had, the music that is played and even the shows you watch while you wait, (a lot of barbershops have big screens in them) and the wise practical advice you could get.

If you are someone who frequents a particular barbershop, you become acquainted with certain people who always show up like recurring characters in a tv show. It can be fascinating.

The barbershop I went to had pictures of black cultural heroes, sports superstars and leaders on the walls like Muhammad Ali, Marcus Garvey, Malcolm X, Bob Marley, Martin Luther King and Fela Kuti.

I Wonder What Fela Would Say?

As I put pen to paper spilling ink
I wonder what Fela Kuti would think
about how the stench of corruption still stinks
and how the people of the land still drinks
from the cup of suffering while still smiling
although recently there's been uprisings
because the people are hungry
and if they could they would all leave the country
The people are being exploited
The whole system is disjointed
I'm sure he would be disappointed
with the leaders who have been appointed
How can songs he released years ago
sound brand new like they are not old?
It's because things don't change they are the same
I really wonder what he would do and say
He would surely call out the president
and everyone crooked in the government
I wish we could be that resilient
Fela Kuti was so brilliant
we need that boldness and confidence
if we are gonna turn around this mess
I'm not an activist
I mean who am I really to speak on this?
but I just can't help wondering
What he would say with his voice thundering
the truth is I just need to listen to his music
he's still speaking to leaders who are abusive

There's no way I can talk about my time living in Nigeria without mentioning the late and great Fela Kuti. He is probably the most famous Nigerian ever globally. He was a musician who created his own style of music called Afrobeat. I was in Nigeria when he was alive. You could hear his music everywhere. You would hear it blasting out of cars, out of windows from people playing it from their homes, on the radio, on TV, it was the soundtrack of Lagos.

There were other types of music you would hear too, fuji, juju, waka, reggae, pop, hip hop, R&B etc etc. Nigeria is full of all kinds of rhythms and melodies. You might see a group of drummers walking down the street playing on an instrument called the "talking drum" just like that but amongst all these sounds Fela stood out because he did something different. He used his music to speak up for the people against the Nigerian government who misused their power. He was really bold because at the time we had military rulers that were ruthless.

I was told that before I was born, the army had attacked and burned down his communal compound that he called "Kalakuta Republic" to the ground. They threw his mother out of a window and she ended up dying because of that. This is all because he dared to be different and speak out against wrongdoings.

He released music frequently and I remember my older cousin that I have mentioned, my beloved Uncle who lived next door and others gathering around the stereo to press play on the latest Fela song that might have just been recorded live at his club called "The Shrine" the night before.

When he died, it was such a big deal. The day of his funeral brought the whole city to a standstill. You could feel the effect of the day just by standing outside. The "go slow" that day was insane. It's like everyone was trying to pay their last respects. It was one of the things that made a huge impression on me as a child. He was truly loved. I didn't understand all his ways but one thing I did get even as a child is that, he was truly a man of the people.

How A Keyboard Became My Cupboard

I used to sneak into a church
when it was empty
and play around with a Yamaha keyboard
plenty hours were spent figuring it out
it sent me
through a portal
I saw my future through melodies
they were telling me who I was meant to be
mentally, I thought of it as an outlet
a vent for me
eventually
I got better at making beats
it was meant for me
time stood still
like it was touched by eternity
like a ghost I silently
kept appearing at this keyboard
composing tracks I imagined
heaven would applaud
It's like I found Narnia
the keyboard was my cupboard
that took me to a new world
upwards, uncluttered
when I mixed those sounds
by nothing I was bothered
In a cluster of sound I was covered
until one day my bubble burst
I was discovered
by the man who was in charge
he kicked me out

I was stubborn
I crept back in, I had to do it
because I found
that the sound I was making
was my way out
this music kept calling
and I had to respond
I felt like I met Aslan
in the great beyond

I never knew I was musical really at first. It was when I got into secondary school and started moving with new friends that I discovered I could hold a note. My friends urged me to audition for the choir. At first I was like "Nah!" but afterwards I did and I actually got in and my first time singing in front of people came out of that.

After a while, I ended up joining another youth choir. We used to meet for practice at a church. There was a keyboard there that I discovered could make beats. I somehow found out how to sequence and compose tracks on it. I honestly don't know how I did it. I just kept fiddling around and after a while I was making track after track. I would record them on a cassette right there. I would then take the recordings home and write my own songs.

I would sneak into the church and make tracks and try to get better. It felt amazing! One day the man in charge, a pastor, found me and told me off! He said I must not do that ever again! I kept sneaking in and at some point, I actually started using the beats I was making to perform at shows. I made a couple of tracks that a friend of mine who is a rapper used for his first songs that got played on the radio.

I think it was at this time I started dreaming of being an artist for real. I couldn't afford to record in a real studio because it was expensive, so I swore to myself that when I got back to London, I would make it happen, somehow.

That keyboard became like that cupboard (or to be more precise that wardrobe) in my favourite book "The Lion, The Witch and The Wardrobe" that opened my imagination up to a whole new world of possibilities. It really did feel like magic when I pressed those keys and made those beats out of nothing! I still make my own beats today. I use my iPhone now though. I guess nowadays I go to Narnia when I touch the screen.

Bar Beach Blues

On sunny days it was the place to be
maybe that's why I was walking down dark streets
I was warned never to do that
Lagos streets could swallow you
but when sadness follows you
you already feel like food
seasoned, burnt and chewed up
now in the streets' belly, in its guts
it can spit you out leaving you hot and feverish
the only cure I sought for was in London I'm homesick

My feet touched the sand and the waves
waved to me
I looked up the sky was clear but my heart and mind were cloudy
and loudly I shouted but crashing waves
drowned out any kind of noise I made
and then the tears came
salty like the ocean
there was no umbrella to shield me
from that rain
Sometimes I revisit that low moment
to remind myself I didn't drown in my emotions

Lagos has lots of beaches. Where I lived in Victoria Island was a 15 min walk from a beach called Bar Beach. When I think back, I really took it for granted. I mean we had family picnics there once in a while but after a while it's like it wasn't exciting anymore.

As I grew up, I came to a point where I had finished my secondary school and the plan was I would go back to London to further my studies. I went to my dad and asked him what the next move would be. He told me to speak to my mother and ask for my passport. One

thing I haven't mentioned yet is I got 4 phone calls a year from my mother. On my birthday, Easter, Christmas and New Year's Day. There were times she missed some of them. I had also been writing her letters and posting them myself since I was 10.

I found a way to call her (phone calls to London were expensive) and when I got through, she told me she wasn't giving me my passport and I should go back to my father and tell him. This was the beginning of almost 4 years that really broke me. I couldn't understand why she was doing this. When I asked why, she said that it was because she felt that my father would just put me on a plane to London and not have anything to do with me anymore. I told her that it wasn't true and even if it came to that, I would take care of myself. She still refused. I was so upset. It was the most frustrating thing ever.

This was all so heart breaking. I went to the British Consulate in Lagos and they said I need proof that I am a citizen before they would help me. My dad had to get someone to get a photocopy of my birth certificate in London. Even with all this the people at the British Consulate told me that I needed to pay them to do a "telex search" in order to verify that I am a British citizen. Even after doing that they said they could not locate my name or record of being a British citizen.

This was the most confusing and lowest time for me. I felt like I had no future. I felt so hurt that my mother would put me through this. I felt like my parents were using me against each other. This brought me to wandering the streets at night and heading to Bar Beach.

Wandering the streets at night in Lagos can be very dangerous but I was so hurt and low that I didn't care. I got to Bar Beach and sat on the sand and cried. I contemplated taking my life. As I sat there I looked around me and realised there was a whole night life happening by the beach. There were clubs and people were dancing, drinking and eating. My beloved uncle was known in this part of town. He saw me and told me to go home! I will never forget this dark period of my life ever.

The Boy In The Corner Of My Heart And Mind

Treated like a rascal
Dizzy
dazed and confused
witty
fearful and wounded
isn't he?
sits
the boy in the corner
of my heart and mind

Gifted and creative
blessed
with insight and wisdom
vexed
looking out of the window
stressed
sits
the boy in the corner
of my heart and mind

Inquisitive and inquiring
seeking
wants to be seen and heard,
He's speaking
but those who are too "grown up"
aren't hearing
the boy in the corner
of my heart and mind

Hungry and thirsty for
meaning
He won't be silenced or ignored
He's healing
He glows and shines when touched
by feelings
is the boy in the corner
of my heart and mind

People say I am a bright and jovial kind of person and they are not wrong. I feel the only reason I am that way is because I have gone through dark and low times. I know that might be a strange thing to say but let me try to explain.

If you are feeling sad, angry, hurt and frustrated, being honest with how you feel and finding a way to healthily express those feelings is so necessary. One of the things that helped me get through is a very old saying that goes "this too shall pass". That just simply means that what you are going through is temporary and will not last forever.

At the time I was so down, it took almost 4 years for a breakthrough to happen and I honestly felt like I would never get through. I felt like my parents weren't listening to me. I felt like they didn't care and were using me against each other. It was the worst feeling ever.

This verse above was inspired by the title of Dizzee Rascal's classic debut album "Boy In Da Corner" When I first heard that album, I didn't like the sound. It felt so harsh and aggressive. It was only after really listening that I understood him. I realised I was similar because of what I went through. I really did think I had no future at all. How wrong I was.

Night Flight

From sitting on the sands of time
with tears in my eyes
I'm sitting on this flight high in the sky
My seat is right at the back
but I don't mind
I'm heading back to
the city of my birth
I smile
this night flight is a metaphor for my life
I've been airborne flying through
turbulence and strife
I've had to take a back seat
and strap my seatbelt tight
I'm not a pilot
I've just been along for the ride
I've got some money in my pocket
and a heart full of dreams
I've got my mind on my future
and by all means
necessary I am determined to succeed
I've rehearsed this in my mind for years
yes indeed
my low times have led to higher learning
I feel a fire burning in my soul as I'm returning
to the streets that my feet first touched
I've waited so long and wanted this so much!

At this point, I feel I have to say that all I am trying to do is give snapshots of my journey through my words. There's so much I have left out. I don't think I can fully communicate how it was but I hope you get a feel of it. I'm just trying to show that the verses I write flow from my experiences in life.

My second stepmother (yes my first one left within a year of me arriving in Lagos and my dad remarried) stepped in and helped me out. After almost 4 years of being in limbo she offered to help me. We did not get along when she first moved in. I was still a kid but older and determined to not let anyone hurt me.

She was the first woman to be the regional director of the ILO (International Labour Organisation) and could make things happen. I had gotten admission into Richmond University and with her help I had been able to get a student visa on my Nigerian passport to travel.

It was all like a dream because it seemed to happen so quickly even though it had taken so long! I was on my way to London on a night flight. My mother did not know I was coming. I didn't let her know because I was upset that she didn't want to give me my British passport. As much as I had grown to love Lagos, I couldn't wait to get back to the city of my birth.

Can I Help You?

In my mind I had rehearsed this
for a very long time
Now I'm here and it seems I came
at a wrong time
I'm sitting by the door just like I did before
but this is in the city of my birth
let's pause
and rewind it back
I had snuck into the building
creeped into the lift
now on the 7th floor I'm chilling
before that I'd taken bus 19 I caught
at Knightsbridge
you see this route was in my thoughts
since I was kid,
I kept it safe in my memory
and replayed it like a favourite melody
Now I'm sitting here waiting it's freezing
My first winter coat in years is keeping
me warm, as I'm sitting in this chair
outside her door that just happened to be there
She's not aware I'm back in the city
where she gave birth to me
in that hospital royal free.

Hours passed but it could not compare
To the 14 years plus that she hadn't been there
would she be happy to see me? I'm full of questions
I'm hungry for answers and thirsty for her presence
It was getting darker shadows lengthened on the wall

Suddenly the lift opened at the end of the hall
A small woman shuffled out of it could that be her?
I thought to myself "no way" though I felt a stir
Of every kind of emotion welling up
my breath quickened I felt my chest swelling up
She got closer now I could see her face
I saw time had drawn lines on her as she gazed
She moved cautiously that's when I realised
There was some fear and worry in her eyes
She asked "can I help you?" not knowing it was me
This was the strangest thing I could hardly speak

When I landed at Heathrow airport, I took a black cab straight from there to my university in Richmond. I was held up for a while at the airport. The people at immigrations weren't going to let me in! I thought to myself "am I about to be deported or what?". What had happened is the student visa that I had got had a slight fault. I felt confident it would be ok as I sat and waited, all they needed to do was call my stepmother and it would be sorted. I mean she was the regional director of the ILO which was like 3 steps below the head of the UN and my papers were legit!

When I got to Uni I had to find somewhere to stay, Richmond is expensive! I tried to find a room everywhere! The school was nice enough to give me an apartment to stay in temporarily which was meant for the student president. He hadn't returned yet because he had broken his leg over the Christmas holidays. I got to stay at his place for 2 weeks! When he came back he actually tried to help me find somewhere to rent. He had crutches and was hopping around. I can't remember his name but I remember he was a very kind Japanese guy.

I ended up making friends with some Nigerian students who allowed me to move in with them and once I settled in, I got on the train and went to look for my mother. In the verses I shared above, everything happened just like that. It is amazing what the mind can remember. It felt good to be back in London even though it was freezing. I hadn't felt such cold for years and it was a shock to my system.

Mum It's Me

"Mum it's me" I said quietly as I stood up
I still had my hood up she looked all shook up
I reached to embrace her but she was frozen
still processing the moment as her door she opened
we walked in and talked for hours
I asked questions
I wondered if she knew how she affected my life's direction
she left the room, went upstairs and came down with an envelope
It was very old
I could see my father wrote
on the front of it my mother's name
there was a note
and an uncashed cheque inside it
his words were cold
"Don't discuss his parentage with anyone
and here's some money for his upkeep"
I was struck dumb
I felt slightly numb my thoughts shattered into pieces
as I realised to him I was his dirty London secret
that he wanted hidden and kept away from sight
after from the fruit forbidden he had taken bites

This was the moment I had been waiting for. I wanted answers to my many questions. Why did she take me to Lagos and leave me there? Why didn't she want to help me come back to London by giving me my passport?

She gave me some answers but not all. She told me that in Igbo tradition if a son is born and the parents weren't together, when he was 7 he was meant to live with his father. She told me that if she hadn't done what she did, he would not have had anything to do with

me. From the letter she showed me, she wanted me to understand my dad would have preferred I was a secret child. I understood her point of view to a degree but didn't fully get it. Her reasons didn't explain why she made it so hard for me to return to London. I don't think she understood how rejected I felt. I had sent her many letters to try to express the pain I felt. She said that she had thrown them all away. We must've talked for almost a whole day.

I went back to University happy that I had seen her again after all these years but still thoughtful. You can't turn back the hands of time. I was here now and had my whole future ahead of me. I had to heal and forgive. I had to adjust to life in London. All through this I had been writing verses. I had to find a way to be heard. I had to find where I fit in and how I could also stand out.

International Style

When I came back to London the place I was born
All I wanted was to now get it on
I looked for platforms, stages to perform
I found open mic events and my songs
Found ears to be heard what was the response?
It was explosive some said I'm the bomb
Other people were like what's going on?
What's with your accent coming from your tongue?
I explained though I was born in London
In Lagos I came up on hip hop that's from
Across the pond where hip hop was born
It shaped my flow and the way that I form
My verses and songs and so on and so on
I'm not being fake when I go on and go on
It's all authentic when I flow on and flow on
It is all real I will shine on and glow on
I know that I sound mixed up
And some people wish that I would fix up
But I'm not broke so I'm like fix what
This is hip hop as the clock tick tocks
You better clock and watch just cotch
Or just ignore me 'cause I won't stop
I'm international not hugging the block
It's Rhythm and Poetry
What is the fuss?

The first times I performed anywhere when I returned to London were at my Uni. I did some performances here and there. I did an open mic poetry night. I did freestyle sessions in the dormitory.

People started knowing this was what I did. I got into a rap battle with some dudes who weren't part of the University and won. (More about that later). I had home advantage but I did beat all 3 of them who were in their crew. I got to perform twice at the biggest night that the University had. It was called "International night" and it was great.

I met a Hip-Hop artist through a mutual friend and he was the first to take me to a studio where I recorded my first demos. This meant a lot to me because in Nigeria I couldn't afford to do this.

I did one of my first open mic performances in a club called Oceans in Hackney and it was great. One of things people would always question me about was my accent. Due to me being born in London, living a little bit in Haverhill, spending all those years in Lagos and being immersed in American hip hop, my accent sounded so weird. I sounded all mixed up. I think today I sound more London but if you really listen I probably don't sound fully like I'm from here.

At the time in the music scene, not sounding totally British meant you would never be accepted. If you sounded like you had a strong American influence you would never be taken seriously. I knew this was going to be a problem.

These days I don't think any of this really matters as much as it used to. The internet has broken down lots of regional walls and sounds and influences travel and mix together. Someone like rap superstar Drake can get away with changing his accent from sounding American to having a Jamaican influence which he will claim comes from his Toronto upbringing and people will give it a pass.

What can I say? It's just my international style.

Memories Of A Telesales Rep

Call after call after call after call
the pressure to make a sale
daily on me it falls
to justify your being here
you must put numbers on the board
so make sure your headset is right
as you twist that phone cord

talk fast think fast learn fast
pick up those tricks of the trade
or you'll be out of this job quickly and unpaid
every call is recorded for "training purposes"
you have to stick to the script
welcome to the circus kid

When they say "not interested"
don't take it personal
they're rejecting the product
not you though you make these calls
actually the calls are automated
you don't dial at all
the program dials from a database
and passes them just like a ball

my accent and voice helped me
to make sales and hit targets
I could sell clouds to the sky
I'd thrive in any market
but this was just a job
to help me pay my bills
I'm glad I left eventually
before my dreams got killed

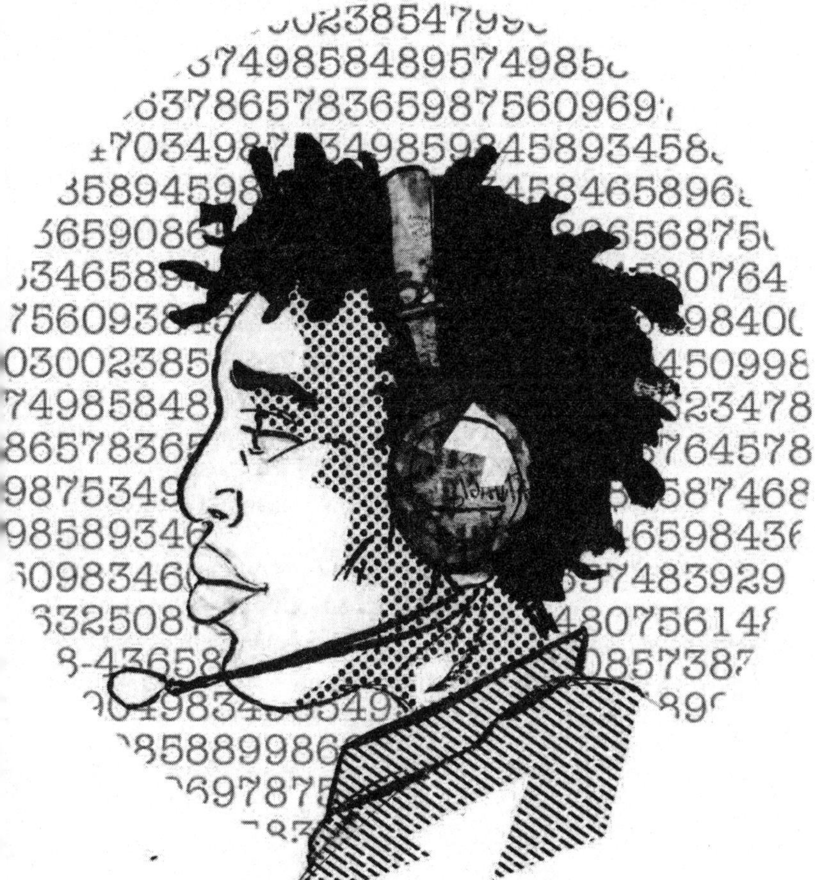

The first job I ever got while I was in University was as a telesales representative in Richmond. I got it with some friends through a job agency. I met a lot of great people there. It is not an easy job at all! There is so much pressure to deal with. The work hours were 6pm to 9pm, so after a day at Uni, I would go there and put in my shift. You had a certain amount of sales that you had to deliver daily and if you didn't, you were close to being fired.

As difficult as this job was, there was something in me that liked the challenge. Also, there was a feeling of comradery you got on the call floor. The jokes and office banter were hilarious on the good days. We also had office parties that were fun. The money wasn't amazing but it was ok for the time.

It wasn't all good though, it was sad when people got fired for not hitting their target. Being successful at making a sale a lot of times was down to the luck of getting a call put through to you from someone who wanted what you were selling. I worked on campaigns that sold credit cards, sky tv and an extra tv channel.

I learnt on the job, lessons that I still use today. Sometimes as you move through life, you might have to do jobs that are not ideal. At some point I did feel trapped there because I didn't know what to do but when the time was right, I handed in my resignation and moved on. That company I worked for no longer exists today.

It Was All A Dream Or Was It?

My friend cracked a joke
and it cracked me up
I laughed so hard
yes I did erupt
with laughter so loud
I'm bursting at the seams
I laughed so much it woke me from my sleep
yes I was laughing in my dreams
but also giggling in reality
it was weird
that my own laughter
woke me up
I pondered this for days and days after

I was freestyling
you know, improvising
it's what I do
so it's not surprising
coming up with verses
off the top of my head
speaking with rhythm
but see I was in bed
I woke myself up rapping
words that came in my dream
this all really happened
the words flowed like a stream
this was strange
almost beyond belief
the lines that woke me from sleep
started a poem I wrote called
"No beef"

Some talk in their sleep
some go sleep walking
someone told me in their dream
they were somersaulting
which led them to rolling
on to the floor
head bumped and bruised
that dream left him sore
I've had dreams that felt great
but got lost in my memory
it's like they tease me saying,
"can you remember me?"
I prefer daydreaming
while wide awake
although laughing and rapping in my dreams
left me amazed

There are different types of dreams. There are dreams you have while asleep and dreams you have while awake. I like to think of myself as a realist, that is one who tries to be rational and "realistic" about things but if I'm honest, I am also a dreamer. There's no way I could create without using my imagination to picture something I want to make happen. This world can be harsh and cruel, it can make you not want to believe in the possibilities of having your aspirations and wishes actually happen.

I really did have a dream and laugh myself awake. It has only happened once and it was so weird hahaha! I really did also rap in my dream and rap myself awake. I have had other times where I was writing in my brain but when I woke up I didn't write anything down. There was a dream I had about not being able to sleep that I can remember having. It was one of those strange dreams you have when you're not quite fully asleep. I should try to write about that one day.

Sometimes the dreams we have don't even make sense, or do they? Our imagination is quite an amazing thing!

Crew Love

You've got my back and I've got yours
It's as simple as that
there's power in numbers so I move with my pack
I won't lose myself in my crowd
who I am is intact
in fact we don't agree on everything
we have heated chats
but we're all cool with each other
in the heat of the moment we chill and give cover
to one another, real friendship is rare
and only few in the long run, will be there
this is a marathon not a sprint let's be clear
some change like the seasons be aware
our energetic banter
is just how we bond
we crack jokes on each other
it's a normal response
when you're just having fun, it's not that deep
although crew love is expensive, it's not that cheap
I move with my squad like we've won the champions league
through the good, bad and ugly 'cause even champions bleed
and even if times change and we go our separate ways
the memories will stay and remain
It's human to have a longing for a sense of belonging
crew love is something that connects
It is a strong thing

I have more than a few poems that touch on friendship. All through the different stages of my journey, friends have played a huge part. That is just life. It is easy to take it for granted so I don't think one can overemphasise the importance of true friends.

Friends helped me discover I was musical, friends helped me sharpen my writing skills. Friends encouraged me to keep going. When I needed somewhere to stay during my first year of University, brand new friends I had just met helped me out. A good friend as I mentioned before helped me navigate my first studio sessions. Another friend introduced me to a producer who was so instrumental in giving me music for my first album. One of my best friends is a guy who has been my studio engineer in his studio for quite a while, shout out to Giuliano!

At key points in your life, I am so sure that having good friends around will help you along in your journey. Crew love forever!

Feel At Home

Even in this hostile environment
that at times can be violent
with slum landlords charging higher rent
it's home bittersweet home some resent
that we call it that
they tell us to go home
"go back to where you came from!"
I'm like whoa!
we've made this home
we won't go
so leave us alone
deal with it you know?

No matter where I go
I'm comfortable in my skin and I know
I don't walk alone, no! no!
although to the naked eye, I'm solo
and I have felt lonely and so low
I've had the blues and my soul groaned
but the rhythm within takes me home
even when far away from all I know

Even if you don't think so
I belong here
that's why from my soul
I sing my song here
I can call out the things I feel
are wrong here
I don't just have to be grateful
For crumbs here

I'll speak truth until I'm done here
I'm from elsewhere but also from here
don't be mad I'm having fun here
In spite of history I've won here

These are words that became lyrics to a song I wrote called "Feel At Home". I have thought about what exactly home is a lot! My father's house in Victoria Island, Lagos where I grew up, has been turned into a home interior design business showroom. I find that so ironic. A long time ago it was leased out by my father's brothers and it will probably never belong to us anymore. I saw a picture of it recently. It has totally changed and is so different from what it looked like.

When I first got back to London, I thought of Lagos a lot. After a while I didn't think of it much because in London, I met friends that made me feel those Lagos home feelings away from Lagos. Now I feel London is home. I have always felt a strong connection to London, I guess because my mother is here. So what exactly is home? I guess it is wherever you feel safe, welcome and you can totally just be yourself.

There are people who try to make you feel unwelcome in the UK, they say things like "go back to where you come from!" and I'm like "I was born in Royal Free hospital in North London, do you want me to go there?" or "I came from my mother's womb, do you want me to go back there? Sorry, I can't go back!". When I first got back to Lagos, my first stepmother used those same words "you better go back to where you came from!" At that time, I wanted to go back to London but it is very strange when racists use the same kind of phrase right here in the UK.

So where have I felt at home? I have felt at home where I feel safe, welcomed and totally myself. I feel at home in my music, I feel at home in my poetry, I feel at home wherever I am on planet earth where a warm welcome is given to me. Even when I have felt unwelcome, I feel at home in my skin and deep within myself.

I Am

I am
me
not you
I am
not your expectations
deal with it
I am
prone to error
yet poised for greatness
I am
real
though sometimes good at faking
I am
a walking contradiction
every step I take
I feel like
I am
contradicting my diction
I am
alive
yet sometimes dead silent
I am
sometimes dead wrong
yet
alive and defiant
I am
deep
yet shallow
in this world
yet not of it

I am
of earth
from dirt
with breath in my lungs
Like I breathe
into this verse
I am
angry
because
I am
hurt
I am
wounded
yet
I am
healing
revealing
yet concealing
visible
yet feel invisible
I am
constantly changing
so by the time
you think you know
who
I am
what you know
is who
I was
because
I am
now
something else

I don't have to say too much about this one. I will say it is one of the very few times I don't rhyme at all. When I wrote it, I wasn't thinking of using it in a rap song or even performing it live.

If you are ever stuck while writing, using this style of making declarations with I am repeatedly, is a good way to get your thoughts and feelings out.

You are a person that has many different sides and you are constantly changing. You are changing because you are growing. Sometimes people around you aren't always aware that you are going through changes on the inside. They want you to be who you always were to them. It is funny we do this to each other because you might be doing that to someone else and not thinking you are. This is why finding a way to communicate the changes you are experiencing is important.

This is probably the oldest poem in this collection. I think I wasn't happy when I wrote this. I felt like people around me were trying to only see me in one kind of way. I remember posting it on Facebook when I wrote it. People really felt this one. I guess they weren't expecting it. People don't always expect you to be different from what they feel they know you as or what they feel you should be.

Straw Man! Straw Man!

We arranged to meet
Face to face
To go toe to toe
Like in a great debate
We named the time
We named the place
It was all set up
You were on your way
You got there first
I came a little late
When I arrived
I was amazed
I overheard you
Rehearse your case
Then it hit me
Right in my face
For other reasons
Is why you came
This was all part
Of your game
You weren't here
To hear me out
To know what I am
All about
I now know what
You came here for
You came to see
A man of straw.

When I first joined social media websites like Facebook, Twitter, Instagram etc, I used to get into a lot of debates with people over different things. After a while I realised that it was a waste of time doing that. Most times people don't really want to understand what the other person is saying.

I wrote this poem when I learnt what a "straw man" argument is. It is when someone who is discussing an issue with you doesn't address what you said but instead makes up something else you didn't say and responds to that avoiding your real point.

You could say "chocolate is great!" And someone else might respond with "what are you saying? Ice cream is great, stop putting down everything else!". This happens so much on social media. The moment I really noticed this, I stopped getting into silly arguments. You can't spend your whole time arguing with strangers online!

Food Fight

Sometimes I wonder
what it would be like
If shepherd's pie
and jollof rice
battled on the mic,
what would that be like?
I know it's kind of crazy
who would win the fight?

Yeah I'm shepherd's pie and let me set this off
just announce me as winner you can't win jollof
I've fed many bellies for years and I won't stop
for long I've been hot in many pots
I've fed many school children all over the place
how many of them have ever had a taste
of what you've got? They know me well
It would take forever to share the stories I tell
yeah I'm shepherd's pie just crown me now!
when I enter into mouths taste buds bow down
I can be prepared in many ways this is a fact
cookery book pages everywhere prove that
so move back, show respect I'm here to stay
no matter what you say jollof, this is my day
see how I burnt jollof rice? You'll get thrown away
I'm done for now what more can I say?

Sometimes I wonder
what it would be like
If shepherd's pie
and jollof rice
battled on the mic,

what would that be like?
I know it's kind of crazy
who would win the fight?

Is that all you've got? Nah this is a mismatch
at least you tried but like potatoes
you're getting mashed
I'm jollof rice straight out of African lands
I've got sauce, I'm spicy while you're so bland
I've fed kings and queens, princesses and princes
my flavour makes mouths water I think it's
clear just my aroma alone defeats you
talk less of how a first taste of me beats you
you might not find me in your cookery books
but my recipe is spreading worldwide take a look
I make taste buds dance like afrobeats
I made bellies sing in many city streets
and I've been doing this since ancient times
I've had countries fighting over me saying
"jollof is mine"
this battle is over, it's clear I'm the winner
even though we're both eaten
I've just had you for dinner

Sometimes I wonder
what it would be like
if shepherd's pie
and jollof rice
battled on the mic,
what would that be like?
I know it's kind of crazy
who would win the fight?

One of the main features of rap music culture is battling. I wouldn't say I am a battle rapper but I have battled before. I mentioned before how in University as I became known to some as an MC in my freshman year, I ended up getting into a rap battle during something called Spring fest.

I was asked to perform and I did. I went to eat and 3 guys were on the mic rapping. I wasn't really listening. After a few minutes of this, someone whispered in my ears "Yo, Karl those guys are dissing you!" I was like "whatever, I am enjoying this burger, what are you talking about?". Then I started listening and could hear them directing some of their lines at me!

I ended up being pulled to the front and the crowd of people egged me on to battle them. To cut a long story short, I battled all 3 of them and won. Now some might say I had home advantage of having this happen in my Uni but I could really freestyle off the top of my head and I gave it to them haha.

What has all this got to do with food? I decided for fun to cross battle rapping with the idea of food battling for what tastes better in my mouth and there you have it a "food fight". Nigerian food can be very spicy and full of flavour and I would definitely say I preferred how my mother's food tasted to what Nan would cook in Haverhill. When I got to Lagos, I had food that tasted amazing like that every single day. In fact I remember my grandmother's cooking to be so full of spices that it would make my eyes water. At first I was like "THIS IS TOO MUCH!!" I felt like my mouth was on fire! After a while you get used to it. My eyes didn't even water anymore. I loved it!!

Jollof rice is a rice dish that originated from the Wolof people of Senegal and Gambia in West Africa. It spread across West Africa and a lot of countries of that region have their own way of cooking it. It has kind of become one of the most popular dishes from West Africa.

Nigerians and Ghanaians especially constantly argue over who has the best jollof rice! I find that hilarious considering the dish didn't originate from either of our countries. I love the dish but I love other ways of cooking rice better! Whenever I say that, a lot of Nigerians look at me like I am out of my mind hahaha!

Empty Train

I'm meant to be good with words
and putting them together to form a verse
but there are times when words truly fail me
and I don't pass the test emotions derail me
the carriage of my thoughts feels empty
and I just sit still and feel plenty hefty
feelings
building gaining momentum
then I start spilling out sentence after sentence
words start rushing out and I must express them
I feel like I might burst if I repress them
I guess then this time patience is the lesson
that I have to learn again through stress and
I know down the line I'll be reminded
this moment I'll rewind it that's why I write this
It's a note to myself posted in my train of thought
I'll look up and read it when I feel caught
and trapped in silence with my voice muted
and feeling stupid because my words aren't fluid
I must remain calm, I must not panic
I'll ride it out and get through times so frantic

I love riding trains. I have always loved getting on a train and going somewhere. I can put on my headphones, turn up my music and enjoy the feeling of the train moving. I love the phrase "train of thought" that is used to express how you are thinking, connecting ideas, reaching a conclusion and going somewhere in your mind.

Writing well can be hard. It takes a lot of practice and even though I have been writing since I was a kid, I always feel I can do better. Sometimes I don't even know what to write about. When I started the above verse, the only idea I had was writing about an empty train, then I related that to how my mind felt empty at the time. I have been in empty train carriages and if you look around them, you can observe things you might not have noticed before.

If you ever feel stuck when writing, one of the tips I always suggest is come up with a theme and then brainstorm as many words as you can that are connected to that theme. Once you have that, you have something to start building with.

One last thing I try to do is to remind myself not to panic. After I wrote my first book and it was received so well and even celebrated, I found myself thinking too much about doing better and living up to the expectations of people who were discovering me. I had to calm down and remind myself of how I started. How I started was like boarding an empty train, putting on my headphones, turning up my music and enjoying the ride.

When You Can't Find The Words

There will be times you'll look for words
and won't find them
like they left quietly without even a "goodbye then"
and silence will be the only thing you hear or even worse sirens
'cause for some the only way they feel heard is violence

There will be times when words seem to go into hiding
and that uncomfortable awkwardness slides in
and you would almost prefer to hear those sad violins
it's almost like silence is teasing you and smiling

and then you'll try again longing for something inspiring
you might even knock on the door where they're residing
and it seems like they're out doing something exciting
the thought of never finding them is frightening

at those times when, words are swallowed by silence
and you wish it would throw them up providing
answers, comfort, some kind of guidance
be reminded, what matters more than words
is the heart and mind behind them

I guess it is safe to say this is the part of the story where I am talking about writing again. I wrote this one day when I was thinking once again about how difficult it is to find words to express your thoughts and feelings.

One day I looked out of my window where I live in East London and what I saw had me really concerned. I saw a large group of young men gathered about to get into a fight. It was about to be a street brawl.

To make it even more serious, I saw a couple of them pull out the longest knives I had ever seen. They were practically swords. In my mind I was like "am I about to witness someone getting seriously hurt?". I couldn't look away but I really didn't want to see anything that would scar my mind.

Their voices got louder and you could feel the tension increase. Suddenly, they all dispersed and started running away. I think they heard the noise of police sirens in the distance. I was very thankful for that because everything was calm again. I was a bit shaken up. This wasn't the first time I had seen something like this.

A lot of disputes could be settled if people could calm down and find the right words and be heard. I think one of the fundamental things people want is to be seen and heard. People want to be understood and respected. It is when people feel disrespected and not understood in extreme cases that violence is resorted to. This is in no way an excuse but a possible explanation. When some people can't find words, they think their fists or weapons are what they need to speak for them.

Do You Know What I Mean?

Sometimes the tone
can be misread
when you communicate
only with text
this may cause someone
to project
meaning into your words
that you never meant

Words come alive
when I'm on a stage
in a way that's different
from on a page
I hope my voice
is being heard
and my heart is felt
behind the words

One can misquote
the words you spoke
also misread
the words you wrote
but you must write
and you must speak
and communicate
what you feel so deep

One of the things you hear people say a lot while speaking is "Do you know what I mean?" or "You get me?" or "Do you know what I'm saying?" or "Nah mean?" or any other variation of people simply just checking if you understood what is being said.

Of all the things I hate, the thing I probably hate the most is being misunderstood. One thing I have had to learn is to accept that not everyone will get what I am saying or I'm about. I understand as a person who is a hip hop artist, there are certain people who will never accept me and I am cool with that. There are people who for their own reasons, refuse to see you for who you are.

I am very careful with words I use. I really do want to clearly communicate my point of view and how I feel. I remember there was a teacher who wanted to book me to come to a school to do an author visit. He seemed to totally mishear what I said in a song. He thought I used some vulgar language which I never used. I don't use vulgar language in my work because I don't want to limit how far my words can travel. That is my choice based on where I see myself going. I don't expect anyone else to agree with me.

There are poets who say "show don't tell" and what they mean is in your writing instead of being direct, descriptive and obvious, you should use a more subtle and indirect way of expressing yourself. They mean paint a picture with your words and let people observe instead of telling them what to see. I understand what they mean and I agree that is one way to do it. I am from the world of Hip Hop where you are more direct.

No matter what technique you decide to use, one thing you have to deal with is the possibility of being misunderstood or even someone reading a totally different meaning into your words. It is something I don't always like but it is what it is. It happens and probably will keep happening.

I battle with the need to explain myself, this is why I have these extra stories tagged on to each poem I share. I won't always do this in every book I write though. There's a saying that goes "Don't waste your time trying to explain yourself to someone who is determined to misunderstand you". I totally get it but struggle with the need to be understood. Do you know what I mean?

Jump

These words jump out of my heart
and land on the page
they jump out of my mouth
when I stand on a stage
I want them to jump through your eyes
and land in your mind
or jump into your ears
when spoken line by line

Hip hop jumpstarted my passion
this drive it gave won't be crashing
before you jump to conclusions
look before you leap to action
deep inside I jump for joy
bouncing back from the blues
sometimes life is a circus
making you jump through hoops

I wonder if I jumped the gun
with the way that I jumped in
I'm not jumping on bandwagons
I had the jump on certain things
please do not jump down my throat
because of things I'm saying
I had to jump at the chance
I'm not jumping ship
I'm staying

I jump from one thing to the next
yes I jump in feet first

I nearly jumped out of my skin
when I was shocked by news that hurt
some try to jump the queue
when they should wait their turn
they want to stay one jump ahead
but had to jump back and learn

Yes I've jumped on some cliches
I'm riding on overused sayings
I know you want to jump on me
it's wordplay, I'm just playing
have I jumped out of the frying pan
and jumped into the fire?
no, I'm jumping up and down
jumping so much
I perspire

I am very aware that when it comes to poetry, there is a difference between hearing a poem performed and reading a poem that is written down. I really do try my best to bridge that gap. I want my words to jump out at you. I want you to hear my voice even when you are just reading what I put down.

The written word is powerful because at the very least you can't mistake what words I am using. If you simply hear me speaking, you can mishear me. The thing is you can misread me too! Your words neatly written down or in my case typed out can be misinterpreted and that is just how it is.

I sincerely believe that poetry was written so that it can be spoken out loud. Human beings first spoke words long before we developed writing. This is why I love rap and spoken word poetry. They are so conversational in style. Some people feel that because they are so conversational that they just can't be poetry. I am aware that how something sounds can affect how you hear it. This is why I have heard poetry spoken that isn't really saying anything but sounds great because of how it was said.

I had someone leave a comment on a YouTube video of a poem I performed saying "this is just a rap" as if saying that meant it wasn't a poem. I guess he found my delivery so conversational and rhythmical that he just couldn't perceive it to be a poem. I found it amusing.

Someone else once asked how I felt about people reading my poetry out loud in a way that is totally different from how I would perform it. I responded that I didn't mind at all and love people putting their own spin on how they deliver what I have written. Let the words jump out however you feel they should.

Reading

When you're reading you're feeding your mind
opening books is like opening doors
in your imagination you will find
an opening where there was only a wall
as the world turns keep turning the pages
each story is like a play acted on stages
reading can you make you see possibilities
reading expands your mental capacity
reading gives you more options and frames of reference
whether it's paperback, hardback, on tablets or audiobooks
reading is relevant
the more you read books the more you can read the times
life is like a book read between the lines
I've got a lot of drive so I must read the signs
I wrote a book, so literally you'll read my mind
I'm a walking audio book, a living book of rhymes
reading is like digging, you dig?
you'll find a goldmine

I can't remember who said "reading and writing are like breathing, reading is breathing in and writing is breathing out" but I totally agree. The above poem was requested by a beloved teacher I met on one of my many travels to schools. She said "write something that encourages reading for World Book Day" and I gladly obliged. The words above were the first words that came out of me. In my mind I had an image of books being doors into different places through your imagination.

When I first wrote this, I didn't include audiobooks but the more I performed it, the more I found myself instinctively including it at that very part of the verse. I was once asked if I would ever do an audiobook. At first I was like, maybe! I wasn't very warm to the idea. You would think I would be since I am a recording artist. I have only listened through an audiobook once.

After talking to a few people about them, I think audiobooks are great! I actually consider all the rap albums, mixtapes and EPs I've released as some form of an audiobook.

I just think it is more important that you are taking in a book than not at all. Reading is important. I do still think there's nothing like opening a brand new book and smelling the fresh pages. There's nothing like holding a book in your hands.

B.A.R.S

Baring all revealing scars
Beautifully articulated rhyme schemes
Bravely announcing real stories
Boldly airing riveting scenes

Breaking away rising sonically
Bouncing around raising souls
Breathing aspirations reaching stars
Blazing away rhythmical scrolls

Beats and rhymes streaming
Battling against raging storms
Becoming alive radiantly shining
Beyond all racial scorn

Born again re-emerging swiftly
Beyond any restrictive situation
Believing against reason supposedly
Blaring aloud resonant salutations

Rap music has grown to be a huge umbrella with many different types that fit underneath it. I was raised on the very lyrical and wordy kind. I like all types of rap but I especially love the type that can be very technical and verbose.

Rappers love talking about bars. Just in case you don't know what they mean, they are just referring to their verses. I have already spoken about how rappers love to rap about rapping in "Rhythm And Poetry". The term bars is taken from sheet music where it just means sections or measures into which a piece of music is divided.

This piece above is one that will sound really good when performed. I do admit it is a bit showy and indulgent but it is one of those fun pieces to write. I cracked my brain thinking about how many acronyms I could make and also I wanted it all to rhyme.

Slang

Slang is the trendy fashion choice of speech
we're forever changing clothes as we speak
you have to dress up your talk for the occasion
the dress code switches
depending on the situation
any fashion statement can become outdated
no matter how in style it is now
it can become antiquated
but some trends remain cool
even when the times change
they become retro and things we still say
'til this day, I still say "bruv" and "cuz"
but strangely enough I no more say "yo blood"
I still say "sis" and "luv" and "fam"
it blew my mind when I found out why jazz artists started
saying "hey man"
because man oh man! I say that all the time
I guess some slang ages well like fine wine
when it's time to dress formally
don't be caught lacking
address and be addressed with respect
or be sent packing

Who doesn't like slang? When I am talking about slang, I mean words, phrases and sayings that are very informal. Slang changes all the time like fashion.

I have gone to different places where the slang they use to express themselves is just particular to them. I have come up with slang words with my friends that only we used. It is fun, as long as you know that you can't use it in every situation.

Sometimes I wonder, who decides when a particular word or phrase is outdated. It seems to naturally happen as people communicate over time. I have observed that certain slang words just didn't catch on the way people thought they would and some just never go away like "cool" for example which came out of how African-Americans spoke back in the 1920s and 1930s.

Black Jazz musicians in the 1940s started using the phrase "Hey Man!" as a greeting to each other because of the racial discrimination in America. They had less rights and they were referred to as "boy" by racists no matter their age to insult them. Today people use that phrase because it's cool and we are just used to saying it. I didn't even know the history of all this until I looked it up.

Slang will never go away, you just have to know when to switch up how you speak depending on where you're at and what situation you're in. It's like knowing what the dress code is for whatever event you're going to be at. Using slang will never go out of style.

When Inspiration Comes

Inspiration comes anytime so be prepared
be open, be aware it's almost like it doesn't care
if you're busy it just comes floating through the air
or knocking on your door with a bright idea
"write this down" it says while I'm walking down the street
other times it says "here's some music make this beat"
one day nature called so I was on the toilet seat
before that I was laidback resting my feet
as I was handling number two in the loo
inspiration came through saying "I have a verse for you"
I was like "where were you when I was chillin' on the couch?"
but inspiration was urgent it said "write this down"
so I pulled my phone out and opened my notes app
tapped the keys and unlocked my heart, in fact
I felt so free for some minutes I forgot
where I was, I finished off then I flushed
I washed my hands, dried them but somehow lost control
and SPLASH! dropped my phone down the toilet bowl
I couldn't believe it, I retrieved it
I clean it off but it didn't come on I'm screaming
I had over 50 pieces written they're so recent
does this mean I've lost them all? I was steaming
I was told it'll be alright put it in rice
I did that, though it sounded like dodgy advice
A few hours later my phone actually came on
I emailed the verses to myself, saved every single one
I was relieved my verses weren't forever gone
the rice I ate that day tasted better on my tongue
I had to go out, I hopped on the underground train
It was rush hour I was squashed with someone's armpit on my face
out of nowhere ideas started popping in my brain
I felt inspiration urging me to write this down again

Inspiration is a very interesting thing to consider. Sometimes you have to wonder about where ideas come from and how they come to you. It is interesting to question how sometimes you can really want to be inspired but it doesn't seem to be happening. When I conduct workshops, I understand that trying to get anyone to write something great in a short period of time can be a really hard thing to demand. In those sessions, I understand I have to try to bring inspiration so that ideas can come and anyone who is part of the session, can get creative and just write freely.

If you have ever heard me speak in person, you might have heard me tell stories of how I am inspired to write on the go. Even most of this book was written on my phone as I moved around. I write while walking, taking the train, on long flights and as I love to also mention, sometimes I write while in the toilet. Inspiration can choose to show up anywhere and at any time.

The great author Octavia Butler said, "Forget inspiration. Habit is more dependable. Habit will sustain you whether you're inspired or not. Habit will help you finish and polish your stories. Inspiration won't. Habit is persistence in practice". I understand what she means even though it sounds a bit harsh. You have to learn how to be disciplined and work at writing even when you are not in the mood. Even when you don't feel like it, you must work at it. It is still nice when inspiration comes though. I guess it comes to those who prepare by being disciplined.

The Silliest Poem I've Written

I once fell asleep while wide awake
after eating a cake that wasn't baked
I chewed some water and drank some bread
before tucking myself in underneath my bed

I had a sweet nightmare the monsters were scared
they screamed and begged that they'd be spared
I went sleepwalking to get some air
came back home and got sat on by a chair

The TV watched me while chewing popcorn
the fire in the fireplace rubbed its hands to keep warm
the book on the table opened up, tried to read the room
the carpet whispered "I've got it covered" but just laid there, blue.

I got up from under the chair and landed on the roof
I looked up and the floor was above my head then "poof"
it all went up in smoke, they say there's no fire without it
did this really happen? Believe me, I really doubt it

I was asked to write a silly poem and I came up with this. This really is the silliest poem I have ever written haha! I think you can safely say this section of this collection will have a few written with humour.

If you really know me, you know that I have jokes for days. I have had a lot of people tell me that I should do stand up comedy. I am not sure that is something I will do but I do throw in lots of jokes when I perform or speak anywhere.

This poem above was inspired by a very old poem. Some say it is so old that it is impossible to say who wrote it. It has a lot of versions and variations. It is part of a type of literature called "Nonsense literature". This is a nonsense verse, or is it?

Laughter can be found in the contradictions of life, in the things that don't make sense and in other unexpected places. I guess we need some nonsense sometimes to make sense of this thing called life haha.

We Need Some New Nursery Rhymes

I think we need some new popular nursery rhymes
to reflect these current and changing times
we all know about that twinkling little star
and that writer still wondering what you are
we've all rowed gently down the stream
now we stream online and touch the screen
we've found out Humpty Dumpty's not an egg-man
that fell off the wall and became a dead man
and yes the wheels on the bus still go round and round
although these days the bus fare costs more than a pound
and old McDonald might have had a farm
but McDonald's have meals that has people charmed
and one, two, three, four, five
most of us haven't caught a fish alive!
and how can a cow jump over the moon?
I wonder as I eat a nice dish with my spoon

We really sang ring a roses and played
only to find out it was all about a plague?!
are spiders still climbing water spouts?
haven't they learned the rain will wash them out?
speaking of water, what's up with Jack and Jill
how come to fetch it they had to go UP a hill?
I wonder if the Mary that had a little lamb
was the same one with the garden (nice one ma'am)
I wrote this on east side of London Town
reporting London Bridge hasn't fallen down
and unlike that black sheep I don't have any wool
but I've got lots of rhymes more than 3 bags full

yes, I think we need some new nursery rhymes
to reflect these current and changing times
I love the old ones still buried in my mind
maybe learning them helped me write these lines

As I have said so many times, when I was a child, the closest I got to poetry at first was learning nursery rhymes. I never had poetry read to me in class. I think it is a great thing being able to learn those fun songs and nursery rhymes with others. It gives you a sense of rhythm and how fun it is to recite something with other people. I guess nursery rhymes prepared me for rap in a way!

I am very sure there are so many of these stories, songs and catchy rhyming phrases that you can find in different cultures. In the verses above, I was trying to mention all the popular ones I can remember learning in a funny way. I wonder if you can spot all of them. I do think it would be great if we can have some new popular nursery rhymes. I actually think some of the catchiest rap songs can be like that.

A Word From A Pigeon

Yeah I know you're looking at me
Yeah you see me out 'ere
I'm a pigeon at a station
I will ride a train with no fear
you humans might not like me
but let me make this quite clear
I have rights you know
so even though you might stare
the worst you can do
is chase me away or just glare
don't forget we've got wings
I can still glide through air
I'll wander into a cafe
and eat food you didn't finish
I'll walk with a strut and be like "what?"
and nibble for a few minutes
some of you are nice
you toss me a few crumbs
some others just detest us
we see you flapping your gums
but I just flap my wings
while you wag your tongue
we won't become extinct
through it all we overcome
we are in many cities
flocks of us are everywhere
we are here to stay
so this world we must share
you humans want to be like us
we see all your planes
but you will never have wings like us
Ah nice! Here is the train!

This was written along with 5 others on the day I was travelling to Wales, to be part of the world famous Hay Festival for the first time ever. I was waiting for my train at Paddington station and was eating breakfast at a café. This pigeon strutted in with all the confidence in the world and was coming straight towards me.

I was sipping on a hot chocolate and nibbling on a croissant. This pigeon kept coming closer and closer. In my mind I was like "is this thing going to keep moving towards me or what?!" It kept coming so I stuck out my foot at it. It moved back but kept coming. It made me think about how comfortable it felt doing that.

When I got on the train, I kept thinking about it and wrote the above verse. My encounter with the pigeon reminded me of another day when I saw a pigeon get on the same tube train I got on in East London.

Animals are fascinating, so while I was on that long train ride to Wales, I thought of other animals and the ideas were flying through my brain...

Hip Hop Dog

Look at my human
I love him so much
He's got his headphones on
Oh I love to watch
as he's nodding his head
to whatever he's vibing to
I wonder if he really knows
how much I love the groove
I'm a fan of Snoop Dogg
as well as DMX
when he barks as he raps
it makes me flex my neck
when he says "where my dogs at?"
I want to say "RIGHT HERE!!"
Instead I growl to myself
(That's how I say "ah yeah")
since I was a puppy
I've heard hip hop everyday
I'm used to sounds from speakers
my belly feels the bass
I wish he would place the headphones
over my ears right now
doesn't he understand?
I want to feel the sound
If I growl he'll think
something is wrong with me
but will he understand
I just want to hear some beats?
I've got a whole verse
that I wrote in my head
If I spit these bars at him
I bet he won't forget

It has always amused me how a few hip hop artists have been inspired by dogs. I mean part of the legendary DMX's whole thing was to bark like a dog on his songs. Snoop Dogg is one of the most famous rappers of all time. I can't imagine him having any other name. If there was ever an artist who had a name that fit perfectly, Snoop Dogg is the definition of that.

I have often wondered how animals experience music. They obviously don't experience music exactly like humans do, or do they? We humans love projecting and attributing human qualities on to animals but sometimes you have to look at them and wonder.

Grime Rat

I crawl through sewers
yeah I know I'm filthy
it is what it is
I know you want to kill me
I hang out where the rubbish is
looking for scraps
I move swiftly
dodging all their traps
there's a whole city of us
beneath many cities
it's a rats life bruv
and it's not pretty
you might see me underground
in tube stations
blink and you'll miss me
my story is ancient
we've been here forever
we survive everything
our teeth are sharp
we chew through many things
we've seen many kings
and many queens
many presidents and prime ministers
have seen
what we can do
and we do it well
and when we work
we give you stories to tell
If you didn't know
we have our own grime scene

It's much more grimier
than anything humans dream
I once crawled into the house
of an artist he went berserk
we've featured heavily
in a lot of Banksy's work
we like to see ourselves
on your city walls
we squeak with glee
when we see the graffiti as we crawl

I don't like rats, please don't be mad if you are reading this and keep one as a pet. I can actually say I hate them. I have seen all kinds of rats. Small ones, big ones, fat ones and so on. I just don't like how they move and just how they are! They move so quickly!

This verse was inspired by a rat that came into my house. I was sitting at home and I saw a sudden movement from the corner of my eye. I knew it was a rat and I was mad! I chased it out but after that, I was restless. I kept thinking it would return and I was super alert!

Grime is a style of music from East London. It emerged out of UK Garage in the early 2000s. UK Garage was bright and fun but as time went on it became a little darker. Grime came along and was darker and more aggressive. It came from youths feeling rejected by the Garage scene. To be part of the Garage scene you had to dress up and be of a certain age. You couldn't just turn up in a hoodie with trainers on. So those who felt rejected and wanted to express how harsh growing up on a council estate could be created their own music.

It was quick like Garage music but was darker and had more bass. It was also led more by MCs who spit lyrics very fast instead of singers who sang catchy songs with bright melodies.

At first I didn't get grime but when I moved to East London, I got it. It is very much a cousin to Hip Hop because it is a voice for those who don't have a voice. The heart of it is people wanting to be seen and heard. Some of the most creative artists the world has ever seen, have come out of the grime scene.

Cat, The Soul Singer

I'm cool I'm smooth go on feel my fur
I can croon I've got tunes can't you hear my purr
you think I'm just a cat
listen I'm a soul singer
I've got lots of melodies behind these whiskers
Oh you don't believe me?
haven't you heard?
I know it sounds crazy and so absurd
only those who want to hear
can hear my voice
so it's really up to you
listen, it's your choice
that hip hop dog once tried to chase me
but I got away back home safely
I jumped into my human's lap and purred sweetly
I hummed more tunes I was completely
caught up in the moment, you hear that sound?
that's me your pet cat, a soul singer now
Oh didn't you know that when I meow
that's me hitting high notes
now I'll take a bow

I like cats. My Nan in Haverhill had one. I have a scar on my wrist because of that cat. I was teasing it and it lashed out and scratched me, I deserved it.

I don't have a pet right now because I just don't think London living will let me have enough time to get one. Also, I am still not sure if I were to have a pet whether it will be a dog or a cat. Honestly, I would like to have both but would they get along? My nan's cat and dog got along so it is possible.

When cats purr, I like to imagine they are singing so that is where the idea to write this verse came from.

Foxy Speech

Yeah I hear when you say "sly like a fox"
but there's much more to me don't put us in a box
by the way "fantastic Mr Fox" was a cute tale
truth is stranger than fiction always without fail
If I could tell you things I've seen at night?
you wouldn't believe me it would blow your mind
It is written in your scriptures that "foxes have holes"
we made space for ourselves whether it's hot or cold
some hunt after us and do that for sport
I have to run for my life many times life is short
yes I'm sly and I'm cunning that's just how I am
my trickery has gotten me out of a lot fam
I don't need to tell you we're all over
we don't even hide sometimes we're getting bolder
one night I made a lot of noise in front of a house
I smiled when I saw this tall guy peeking out
of his window, he looked very scared
he banged on the glass to scare me I didn't care
we can make ourselves heard if we want
just leave us alone humans, call off the hunt!

In Lagos I never saw a fox. I don't think we have foxes in Nigeria, if I am wrong let me know! So when I landed back in London and went to University in Richmond, seeing a fox at night wandering the streets for the first time was like wow!

One of my favourite books as a child was "Fantastic Mr. Fox" I read it while in primary school in Lagos. Foxes to me were just creatures in books. You grow up hearing the phrase "Sly like a fox" and you just accept that foxes are cunning creatures.

One night I was awakened by the weirdest sound ever. When I looked out my window a fox was right there making this weird loud sound. It was a fox all alone snarling and I was kind of amazed! I realised at that moment that I had never heard what a fox sounded like before. It kept making this noise, so I tapped on the window to try to scare it away. After it had done this for a few seconds, it casually walked away.

I have seen a few foxes around my area and they seem to be getting more comfortable to stroll around. Sometimes they don't even wait for it to be dark! I started imagining what that fox was trying to say and that verse emerged.

The Butterfly Effect

Have you ever had one of those
bad days
sad you ever woke up
those mad days
the last straw that broke the camel's back kind
those kind of days when you can't find
any silver lining or reason or meaning
no sensible pattern only dark feelings
sometimes those days can last for days
and leave you dazed by the blues grazed
so random like you've been hit by strays
like life got trigger happy and just blazed
I had a day like that and a butterfly came
and landed on my hand like it knew my pain
It's like time stood still with a smile and looked
It's beauty stole the moment
this beautiful crook
for a brief moment lifted my blues
reminding me that I'm probably in a cocoon
like a caterpillar who will emerge soon
as this butterfly must've done before this time
and as I had that realisation
it took flight

Sometimes it takes something so small to make a big difference. As I have been writing this book up to this point, I have been thinking of all the small things as well as big things that have made me who I am.

A small kind act that you do can change someone's whole day. I think that is so powerful. You might think you are small and insignificant but you're not!

As a Hip Hop artist, a lot of people tell me "you're underrated" They say this because when they hear my music and it sounds good to them, they expect me to be famous and a popular superstar. I see things differently. If what I do has touched one person and made a difference, then it's been worth it. The funny thing is what I do touched me first before anyone else.

Amazing and great things can be found in the small moments that are special to you. It can be something as simple as a butterfly randomly landing on your hand on a day when you felt down.

This was the last of the 6 poems I wrote on my trip to the Hay Festival, in fact I was writing this one as I got off the train and finished it when I was having lunch there! I guess I had animals and a butterfly on my mind

¯_(ツ)_/¯

Forwards And Backwards

I've heard of 10 green bottles
hanging on the wall
I've heard a cat has 9 lives
but what if it lost them all?
I once ate 8 berries
all in one go
I was weak for 7 days
I had a bad cold
I saw a man play a guitar
it had 6 strings
everyday my 5 senses
keep tingling
there are 4 seasons
summer is my favourite
I eat 3 meals a day
good food, I savour it
you have 2 ears
so please hear me out
this is 1 poem you can read
forwards and backwards out loud!

I was asked to write a verse for a compilation and this is what I came up with one day. I have always admired those people who can write a verse that works forwards and backwards. This was my first attempt at something like this for fun. This kind of poetry is called reverse poetry. This poem however doesn't have a totally different meaning when you read it backwards, or does it? You tell me!

Reading it forwards makes it a rhyming poem. Reading it backwards from the bottom up, makes it a poem that doesn't rhyme. Two poems with two different styles for the price of one. Nice bargain, right?

Late Bloomer/Blooming Late

Maybe I'm late, no you won't hear me say that
It won't escape my lips that saying goes way back
I'm speaking of saying I'm a late bloomer
saying I didn't have the courage to be myself sooner
It takes time to blossom, longer for some though
future seeds are sown some die, some grow
It took time to find my feet planted in this field
stung by nettles almost choked by weeds I kneeled
great expectations weighed on me had my head bowed
I couldn't stand up I was on shaky ground
In reality I wasn't walking I was falling down
speaking out not thinking what I was talking about
loads of confidence I must've really had a bigger mouth
I really thought I knew it all and had it figured out
so far ahead I thought in my mind
so sure I'm ahead of my time

This is another piece that works forwards and backwards. I actually recorded this as a rap song where I rap it forwards top down and then in the second verse, I rap it from the bottom up. I never released it. I might do that someday.

I feel like I am a late bloomer. What does that mean you ask? It means I feel like it took me a while to really become who I am today. It means sometimes when I used to compare myself to others, I felt like they had gone further than I had in what they were doing. I felt like it took time for me to grow and develop. You know what? Now I realise that it is ok! Sometimes things that last longer, take longer to develop and grow.

Everyone is on their own path. Everyone is different. You might feel like you are slower than others in certain things, it really is ok. As long as you keep going and don't give up. You only feel you are late if you keep comparing yourself to others. Just be you.

When It Strikes 12

I'm not one to brag and boast but one must let you know
that one day I sat and wrote more than one goal
and to my surprise too many times too many small minds
thought my dreams were too big for my size
but I've met more than three wise men and women
and more insight than 3D glasses was given
for me it was a forecast, foreshadowing my future
I moved with foresight forerunners are my tutors
I don't need more than five minutes to make my point
though I could take five more and bend time like it's got joints
that are flexible some believe we've got 6 senses is that sensible?
maybe it is 'cause intuition is incredible
across the seven continents there's more than seven billion
human beings,
each week, seven days we're living 'em
I think I ate a large plate of words but still don't know enough
Oh no, I think I overate so now I'm throwing up
more than nine verses and nine poems some can't stand it
when I was eight there wasn't eight there were nine planets
I read something about ten commandments on stone tablets
I know it's random but does 10 Downing Street have an attic?
there are eleven players on each team in football matches
but red cards reduce that number when things get drastic
and in each twelve months
if I took a twelfth letter
When the clock strikes twelve
each year I bounce back better

I don't think this style has a name but I am very aware of rappers doing verses with numbers, countdown style. I have done it in a song called "Overcomer" before. It is something cool to attempt where you try to find a way to countdown from 10 to 1 in a verse.

If you want to try writing something like this, one thing to do is think of every idea connected to each number, write it down, then use it to build a verse. It doesn't have to be a rhyming verse. The most important thing is to think of how to make your ideas link up.

In this one I reversed the order and did 1 to 12. The last four lines contain a riddle. I wonder if you can decipher what I meant there? I would love to know.

North, East, West, South

There once was a man from the south
who was always playing about
when it was time to be serious
he kept being an idiot
and ended up with his foot in his mouth

There once was a boy from the north
born on December twenty fourth
would you believe
that every Christmas Eve
He opened his presents of course!

There once was a girl from the west
who was so sure that she was the best
It proved to be true
In all she chose to do
except for that one time she made a big mess

There was this lady from the east
who met a man from the south at a feast
he acted so awkward
talking to him was torture
he kept making a meal of his feet

This was just something else I wrote for fun. Sometimes when I watch
the news this is what it sounds like to me. The title of this verse is an
acronym for the word NEWS.

I have often wondered where the word "news" comes from. I found out the word developed as a special use of the plural form of "new" in the 14th century. It was like the French word "nouvelles" and German word "Neues" which both mean new. So "news" is connected to the presentation of new information (well it's supposed to be hehehe)

Another piece of random trivia is my name "Nova" is from the Latin word "novus" which means new as well and a Nova or supernova is a new star that becomes brighter as the result of an explosion. I chose that as my MC name because of this meaning. The whole idea is when I express myself creatively it felt like an explosion and I felt like glowing bright. I know that sounds a bit extra and over the top but that is honestly how I feel haha!

The word "novel" which is another name for a book (which is a word I don't hear used that much these days) is all tied into this. A novel was a new story you read.

The fact that the word news is made up of letters of the 4 cardinal directions on a map is totally coincidental but fits so beautifully if you think about it. Daily we receive news from all directions, north, east, west and south!

The Misinformation Age

We're in a time when everyone thinks their opinion is truth
they think every thought they spew is absolute
everyone seems to be an expert and a critic
that seeks to speak for everyone
I don't get it
conspiracy theories are making souls grow weary
the fear of the unknown has got people feeling eerie
we have a lot of information but very little truth
a lot of speculation but hardly any proof
some think everything is true on YouTube
That's why perceptions are skewed on cue
some think everything has a message subliminal
but if you say truth is in you,
how can you continue
to live in fear
and remain paranoid
tossed to and fro by deceptions and decoys
lack of knowledge of the truth it destroys
sadly empty vessels still make the loudest noise
we have a lot of information
but little revelation
that's why there's hardly transformation of situations
what are you buying into?
what holds your attention?
'cause what holds your attention
holds you like detention

This verse was originally part of a song I wrote in 2011 called "Emergency Call" that ended up on an album released in 2012 called "Delayed But Not Denied"

In 2015 I took part of the song "911" and this verse above is what I had. I just kept it in my mind tucked away. By the time 2019 came around, I was a national poetry day ambassador and the theme that year was "In Poetry, Truth" and I was asked if I had something on the theme of truth and I remembered this verse tucked away in my mind. I recorded a video for it and it is still on the National Poetry Day website now.

I shared all that to show how the journey of a poem can be sometimes. When I first wrote this I never knew it would end up where it did. This is why I say treasure what you write because you just never know.

The idea of truth has been on my mind since I was a kid. We are truly in a time where knowing the truth is even more important but at the same time so much misinformation floats around. It's an ironic thing that in the what is called the "Information age" that misinformation is more common, but that's how it is.

People seem more interested in what they think and already believe being true than actually finding out what the truth is. It's hard to admit that they might be wrong.

On the internet you can find anything that supports what you already believe. There are even websites full of fake news and satire just for that reason. This is why you must be extra careful about what source you get information from.

All this means is you have to have a mind that questions things and is ok with finding out you could be wrong. No one knows everything. Opinions don't have to be permanent. It's ok to change your opinion based on new information that is correct. Be informed not just opinionated. Have the heart of a seeker of truth not the arrogant attitude that you are always right.

Algorithm And Poetry

Click
Send
Like
Then
Repost
Do it again

For such a time as this I am here
I don't mumble my words I am clear
this climate can choke you it's filled with fear
I breeze through I'm clearing the atmosphere
this digital era we are in
has got misinformation spreading
be conscious of what you're sending
don't just follow blindly to blend in
comparison is still the thief of joy
don't be distracted it's a decoy
your sense of self-worth it can destroy
the fear of missing out it is deep boy
we touch our screen to stay in touch
but are we out of touch as we clutch
our smartphones in a world dumbed down
I know I must but I can't log out

So many folks wanna go viral
to feel famous to them it's vital
you would think it's key to their survival
the way they shoot for it like a rifle
but hey shoot your shot
It's all banter though it's a lot
why so serious they won't stop

more novelty tunes will pop
and the trollers will just troll
I say don't feed 'em yeah that's cold
they just want attention that's old
don't engage 'em it takes its toll
and don't fall for the click bait
It is a con it is a trick mate
To drive traffic to their websites ay!
It's all a hustle to make pay!

This digital generation
is seeking for validation
filled with longing and frustration
The genesis of this revelation
is nothing new
the difference is we have new tools
technological breakthroughs
smartphones in the hands of fools
what's real? It's like you get to choose
many believe in fake news
as long it makes you feel good
the dopamine it feels true
who's controlling the narrative?
keep questioning keep on challenging
for your mind keep on battling
shake some tables and rattle them.

As a person who was a kid that grew up without the internet, it is crazy to think that you reading my words might be born into a world where having the internet freely available is normal.

As a teenager getting the internet was great for me. I could stay in touch with my friends around the world via emails and chatting online. I had access to any song at any time because of file sharing.

It was great. Now I have a smartphone that does all that and even more. It is how I wrote the majority of this book.

I have created music from scratch for over 10 full projects on my iPhone that you can hear anytime, anywhere on all streaming services worldwide!! If I could go back in time and tell myself sitting at that keyboard making my first beats that this would be possible, my mind would not have been able to understand it.

Even though technology has advanced, the issues humans have faced are still the same. I think in a way it is tougher for young people though in other ways it's cool to have access to all this technology.

As a young person being accepted, liked and popular is something that is held highly as something to be desired. As an adult these things are things that are still chased by many. I am always asked "how many YouTube subscribers do you have?" "How many TikTok followers do you have?" "Have you ever gone viral?" "Are you verified?" and things like that. I feel like I am asked these things by people who want to know if I'm "cool" enough because that's what they desire.

I honestly don't really care about that because I have found out that knowing who you are within is more powerful and important than those things. Your importance, your worth and that which makes you special goes deeper than going viral online or being popular. You have to believe that and know that deep inside for yourself.

Before I knew about social media, I was already me writing my poetry and creating beats. Before even finding out I could do all that, I am who I am, a human being, living out my life, living my story. Ultimately that is all that matters.

See Through My Eyes

I aim to speak truth using poetic devices
with words I'll be incisive
sharp like a new knife is
It puzzles me when some say it's divisive
when truth separates us
from what keeps us divided
our shared humanity is what makes us united
unity in diversity why do some fight it?
how can my dignity make some feel slighted?
is the lowering of others what keeps their pride ignited?
unity doesn't have to mean uniformity
or conformity to something I am not normally
experiences keep swarming me
transforming me
this caterpillar is now a butterfly soaring free
this rhythm and poetry might make you
see what I see
you might think differently,
we can agree to disagree
or find our feet standing on common ground
that is level and even
is that odd?
how does that sound?

My sound mind amplifies these lines that resonate
your head nods in agreement eardrums vibrate
or maybe you're reading these lines
seeing into my mind
and somehow you can hear
my voice captured in time

It's a matter of time
my vision will capture your mind
a kaleidoscope of feelings and thoughts
you will find
words are my colours
my voice is the paint brush
emotions saturate this portrait
visions so lush
swirl into your imagination
images flashing cause fascination
when days are grey and I lose all patience
I dress my mind up with lines and take a vacation
verses transport me without changing location
no passport or visa needed
elation
is found in this moment piercing the mundane
see through my eyes,
watch this frozen world melt away

I wrote this because the theme for National Poetry Day in 2020 was "Vision, see it like a poet" I got an e-mail from them asking if I had anything and this was the first thing I wrote.

One of the most powerful things poetry and literature in general does is you get to see through the eyes of someone else. It is always my hope that you can see what I see and feel what I feel when you read my words.

You might not have experienced exactly what I have but as a human being we all share similar emotions. We all ask similar questions. It's ok to see how similar we are as well as also acknowledging differences.

The one part of this piece that I fear can be misunderstood is where I say, "You might think differently, we can agree to disagree" and I'll tell you why. There are many things we can agree to disagree on. For example, I think apple juice is better than orange juice. It's not that I don't like orange juice but I think apple juice is better. You might think differently and like orange juice better. Cool. End of discussion.

When it comes to my worth as a human being and whether my life matters as much as anyone else's then it is not a matter of "agreeing to disagree". If you disagree about something like that, then that is something else. My dignity as a human being isn't something up for debate and neither should yours be either. When it comes to human rights, being treated fairly, respected, being seen as a human being that has worth, this is not a discussion or debate anymore. No matter who you are, or where you're from, you are born with those, they are yours, end of.

Change

Change is always happening
It's a fact my friend
It's like fads and trends
like I used to write poems
with pads and pens
now I type them in my phone
I've still got stacks of them
them being notebooks
I once wrote in
my head in the clouds
daydreaming and floating
even when sitting still
we're in motion
as the earth rotates
change isn't slowing
growth brings change
and as we are growing
life makes me wonder
with eyes wide open
the seasons run their annual relay
Spring passes the baton to Summer
Whose quick pace
and speed runs it's lap hands over to autumn
Autumn is cool but not cooler than Winter
I'm talking about change
even when things seem the same
It has a mysterious way about it
that seems strange
like it seems to happen suddenly
it's hard to explain
even change changes I mean that's its name!

change is always happening
It's a fact my friend
It's like fads and trends
like I used to write poems
with pads and pens
now I type them in my phone
and I'm rapping them

The other day I went through stacks and stacks of old notebooks. I read verses that I forgot I had written. I can't even lie, a lot of what I read made me cringe, YIKES! Maybe I am just my own worst critic. Looking through my old writing was like looking at photographs of myself wearing clothes that are now out of style!

I have definitely changed how I write over time and what I write about and it will continue to change. This is why I am such a big encourager of anyone who wants to try writing. People think I was born being good at this. I struggle even with believing I am good now sometimes! I had to keep doing it to get to a place where I felt comfortable even sharing at all!

I wrote this piece very quickly. That isn't a brag at all. I knew I had to write it because I was told this was going to be needed on a specific date. I left it until the day before it was going to be videoed to write it. I didn't even feel it was great but people really liked this one!

Change in life happens and that is just the way it is! I am a person that doesn't like things changing any old how. I once had a favourite pair of shoes that were so comfortable. I wore them for so long that one day when I went out, I could feel the ground. Basically, my shoe was so worn out, the soles on one of them ripped! I refused to change them but was forced to. I could never find a pair exactly like them again.

If you are like me and have been through so many changes that you had no control over, you might not want too many sudden changes. It can be so jarring. The thing is, even change changes because that's its name!

To The Curious Hearts And Minds

It's ok to be curious, it's ok to ask questions
life is a mystery that invites investigations
and on your quest pay attention to clues
perceptions and views get stretched and reviewed
curious minds asked why humans couldn't fly
and in time we now glide in planes in the sky
curious minds had serious thoughts
wondering how it would be possible to talk
to someone from a distance while at home
through trial and error emerged the first telephone
and now we video call, it's now normal
curious minds in past times could only dream
of how you talk to
your loved ones and friends at that click of a button
or the touch of a screen you're in touch all of a sudden
curious minds have looked into space
we're still searching and wondering about our place
in the greater scheme of things we're still seeking
curious minds collide with deep questions week out and week in
curious minds ask how come all people
aren't treated as equal and how come evil seems to
speak to the world with a louder voice
curious minds ask "how do we cut through that noise?"
it's ok to be curious, it's ok to ask questions
life is a mystery that invites investigations
and on your quest pay attention to clues
curiosity leads to truth
and a much broader view

I've always been a curious kind of person and I think that's not a bad thing. One day I was curious and typed my name into google. When you do that frequently asked questions pop up to try to complete your sentence for you.

When I saw some of the frequently asked questions connected with my name it made me laugh out loud. I get it, the more places I've been to and the more people I am exposed to, the more curious people get about me and that's ok. Here's a tip though, the place to really know me is in my music. I reveal so much through all the music I have put out. I am a private person but I really do say a lot through my music.

It's ok to be curious, be prepared for what you discover when you get curious about something. Curiosity is what got me into making music. If I didn't get curious about that old keyboard I found, I probably wouldn't be making music today. Be curious. Stay curious.

The Questions

Have you ever felt so curious and felt a tugging in your mind?
that the next thing you ask is Who? What? When? Where? And Why?
like who said this or that is true and when did they say it?
and what was their point? Why did they choose to relay it?
and where did all this happen? and where are they now?
can anyone tell me their current whereabouts?
then you start wondering, why do I even care?
What made me so curious? When did this start and where?
Who am I to ask these questions? Who cares who I am?
I wonder who else feels like I do, who else understands?
When will all these questions stop flooding my mind?
When will there be a turning of the tide?
Why do things happen as they do as time passes by?
I'm sure others have asked all this so why ask why?
Have you ever felt so curious and felt a tugging in your mind?
that the next thing you ask is Who? What? When? Where? And Why?

A lot of times when we ask questions we are asking a Who? What? Where? When? And Why? and maybe also How?" kind of question. I didn't use how in the verse above but you could come up with poems using that or any of these to address a topic or theme you are curious about.

Just think of all the questions you could ask and by the time you have filled your page with these questions you can arrange them however you please and you have a poem. It is as simple as that. The part that isn't always simple is getting the answers to your questions. I am still seeking answers to a lot of mine.

Scribbling Dreams

No need say I'm lit this is literature
rhythm and poetry with my vocal signature
I withdraw inner riches with mic checks
So my vocal signature on mic checks is priceless
you can take it to the bank
word is bond
my stock rises like my vibrations
I invest my time and I trade with my talent
I see a return and feel challenged to balance
and make sure things weigh up
my words carry weight I don't just say stuff
that is empty
nah the volume of my thoughts is a lot
matters contained occupy space heavy thoughts
and feelings build up and spill out
this poetic language is overflowing no doubt
there's no drought, there's no famine
although some are famished
well feast on this banquet

Talk is cheap but my speech is expensive
'cause I've paid the price to speak each sentence
I deliver 'em like a court judge
after weighing up the evidence I won't budge
It's beyond all reasonable doubt
the truth is self-evident I'm speaking it out
yes I show and prove as I drop these jewels
'cause I was raised in the golden age that's true
knowledge and wisdom leaps out of my mouth
dives into your ears lands in your mind wow
and meets understanding there

I enrich souls with these words I share
So you can get involved or just stand and stare
I don't really care 'cause as long as I'm here, yeah
I'll keep on spittin' these verses I'm living
these words that I'm giving are so sincere

This gift of rhyme and rhythm
that I've been given
the life I'm living
the lines I'm spitting
the mic I'm gripping
as time is slipping
my mind is flipping
man listen
sometimes I think my mind is tripping
but maybe it is just a coping mechanism
an open recognition that we're in a broken system
I was a young fool hoping for some wisdom
these scrolls I've written is showing my souls condition
my inner child deals with issues of abandonment
I guess that's why I show presence when I stand and vent
at live events where my time is spent
expressing rhythm and poetry that's so intense
I'm content with my intent and content
I open doors in your imagination such a gent
I am as I speak with eloquence and excellence
showing intelligence and walking with confidence

I scribble this, scribble that
I scribble down rhythm and poetry
right across the map (Dream Big!)

I got invited to be part of the Hay Festival's scribblers tour. It was a 5 city tour of Wales and on the tour with me were amazing authors Jenny Valentine and Emma Carrol.

The moment I knew I was going to be on the tour, I felt inspired to write a song which I ended up calling "Scribbling Dreams". My plan was to perform it at every stop of the tour. I also planned to release it as a single on all streaming services which I did.

The lyrics above were a whole set of verses I had in my head. Sometimes I write long verses and just memorise them. It is an exercise I do. I also do it in case I am in a situation where I need something fresh to recite. This is a very "rapper" thing to do. I have a lot of these kinds of verses in my memory.

When I write I want to be as witty and as intelligent as possible. I want to communicate knowledge, wisdom and understanding in a fun and cool way. I want to have lines that will make anyone want to listen to or read over and over again. One thing I will say for younger readers especially is if there are words that you are not sure you get the meaning of, you can look them up with a dictionary. Another thing I will say is as you learn more, you probably end up understanding more. I remember watching a film I watched years ago as a kid and now watching when I've grown up, it's like it was a whole new film!

Like I have said before I feel like words are magical. You really need to understand that words, understanding their meanings and how to use them is powerful. It is still a wonder to me that finding ways to make words fit together and reciting them with rhythm has literally made a lot of my dreams come true.

All this while I have been scribbling dreams and seeing them happen! There's a lyric video for this on my YouTube channel: KarlNova. Hearing the words with the music helps you enjoy it more in a different and fun way!

Tell It As It Is

I'm an artist, a poet of the spoken type
I've got humour I guess I am the joking type
somehow I pry closed minds open right?
with words stitched together I'm hoping I,
connect with you,
look I was a broken guy
in some ways I still am, my woken mind
is very inquisitive, like oceans I'm
quite deep and also in motion like
time is, or is it, I've chosen rhymes
to express the fire inside in frozen times
sometimes I watch clouds floating by
and without thinking start composing lines
I opened my mouth wide at open mic
events learnt how to get my vocals right
I think global but really I'm a local guy
my stream of consciousness is rolling by

I walk my talk you'll see me strolling by
coming to grips with reality holding tight
but also I let go 'cause moments like
this are a release from my soul I shine
I'll work it out until it's closing time
I can work a crowd exploding bright
with joy deep inside it's showing right?
it's pretty obvious I'm sure you notice I
come alive and get into my zone inside
there's been times I have felt alone inside
rhythm and poetry helps me cope with life

it's therapy for me my emotions might
have overwhelmed me, made me choke inside
but I pour it all out and find hope inside
frozen hearts melt when these molten lines
travel through ears and eyes they open minds

Life is not a gamble I'm not holding dice
to me it's a concert so I'm holding mics
when I get hurt I won't be holding spite
or holding a grudge I won't hold it inside
I let go in my soul and keep glowing bright
it's showtime grab a ticket the show is life
where we're all on stage you know the hype
is not to be believed the show goes on right?
current affairs got me saying whoa and why?!
but life keeps moving like ocean tides
the music in my heart has potent vibes
it's strong enough to uplift and cause souls to rise
and hear this I'm not the token guy
I'm not a stereotype I break moulds alright?
when days get dark with much colder nights
I turn up the heat within, it smoulders, nice.

This is something I wrote with the aim of using the same rhyming scheme for the whole thing. I wanted to see how long I could go sticking to that formula. This is one of those verses I did just for exercise and also to have ready for any situation where I might need to have something new to perform.

A standard rap verse is what we rappers call "16 bars" which is just a fanciful way to say 16 lines or 8 rhyming couplets. Sometimes we rappers/MCs might go for 32 bars. I originally wrote this as a 48 bar long verse.

Later on, I created some music and broke it into 3 verses of 16 bars each. I am sure someone has read up to here and is thinking "wow I didn't know rap was so technical and mathematical". Well that is how it is! I wouldn't say there are rigid rules, but there are guidelines that help you structure your writing.

I also wanted to use this piece to express where I saw myself as an artist. I feel like I have grown and every now and then I find myself reflecting a lot. This leads to me writing something like this. I love performing this one especially without music.

Summer Love

How they met was like destiny or fate
or maybe random then they had their first date
they met up at this little cafe
he had some tea she had a latte
they went back and forth with the small talk
that date morphed into long walks
you know how it is when boy meets girl
girl meets boy, boy promises the world
they're trying to figure out if it's love or lust
maybe it's just infatuation, a crush
they decided to slow down and not rush
they were always together
and never lost touch
he likes her, she likes him
so why do I think the chances are slim
that what they have will last, I think
it's just summer love it won't even see Spring

Summer's coming to an end, here comes Autumn
did they fall in love? The heat is scorching
like the way she felt for him
but did he feel
that same fire within?
the small talk morphed to deeper conversation
they talked a lot about their situation
she was thinking way beyond the summer
but on his calendar it's like there were no numbers
he looked at her and said
"let's live for the moment"
she replied,
"but our future, we have to own it"

he said,
"ain't ya heard 'the future is now'?"
she said
"I hear what you're saying, please tell me how"
He said
"listen focus on the present
Let's take one day at a time and lessen
your worry about how things will turn out..."
she interjected
"what if things burn out?"
he paused for minute
he looked away into the distance
he drank from his cup
until his whole drink was finished
she waited for his answer
and searched his face while drinking
the words "summer love"
rang in his mind as he was thinking

Writing storytelling verses about a totally made-up situation is a challenge I return to again and again. In this one I wanted to write a story that has an open ending.

When I do write this way, I try to end the verse in a way that lets you guess different ways the story can go. I think that is fun. How things turn out is up to your imagination. It's like you get to be part of creating the story.

As you grow and get to the age of beginning to have feelings of liking someone, life takes a whole other turn and you have to make decisions. I am no relationship counsellor but my only advice would be to take your time and don't rush. That's all I have to say about that! Haha!

Tracks

You wave at me and beckon me over
you gave me a hug and as soon as I got closer
your voice is one I am familiar with
you comfort me, I'm far away from where I live
so even though I'm feeling off key
you make sure I'm in tune
you keep me on beat
you're my soundtrack on strange streets
I row gently down your stream
merrily merrily merrily life is but a dream
but I'm wide awake though I take note
of the notes you use to soothe my blues
and change my grey days to colourful hues
a kaleidoscope I view through the gloom
and when I get red hot with rage
your keys opened my cage
of feelings that spilled over on a page
and somehow transported me to the stage
I'm at home right now
your rhythm in my mind now
reminding me of my quickening pulse
I'm alive now!
I can't speak the language
hello and thank you is all I can manage
as I sit and ride
in this Shanghai metro carriage
but you're universal as stated by that old cliché
that I now comprehend in a new way
you've been with me since birth
hummed to me before my toes touched earth
my life began when a beat played in my chest
we are all music making tracks step after step

All I have wanted is to be creative for a living. I have held on to that dream through everything and somehow it has taken me to places I never thought I would ever be. I have travelled to Slovakia, Turkey, Cyprus, Switzerland, Germany, Luxembourg and so many other places because of what I do. When I was so low and sad sitting on that beach in Lagos, I could not even see myself doing this even though I really wanted to keep creating.

I wrote the verse above in Shanghai, China. I was on a tour of Mongolia and China that lasted almost a whole month. It is the furthest I have been away from London to tour ever. I was all by myself. I really did feel very lonely at one point in China but once I got used to being there, I was fine.

Before I travelled, I felt a bit scared but I really didn't have to worry. I had people in every city I went to help me. Yes, I had help in all 5 of them. Beijing, Suzhou, Shanghai, Hangzhou and Qingdao. I spent 5 days in Ulaanbaatar, Mongolia before moving around China.

Music is something that makes me feel comfortable no matter where I am. There's nothing like playing an album or songs you like to make you feel at home no matter where you are. It is also really comforting when a song you love randomly comes on when you're in a public place faraway from all you know. I am fortunate that I can compose music on the go as well. I can create beats right on my smartphone and I make quite a lot of music as I move around.

While in Mongolia and China I met some very friendly people. I remember sitting in a station in Beijing waiting for my train and a family sat next to me. They couldn't speak English but they tried to have a conversation with me. It was a man, his wife and 2 small children. They offered me fruit and after bowing they went to board their train. That has never happened to me in London!

Picture Me At A Qingdao Pier

Touched down in Qingdao
now I'm sitting at the pier
a Chinese couple appeared peering at me I hear
the woman speaking excitedly pointing at me
gesturing for her man
to point his phone at me
so happy
she seemed to be
I'm now thinking "is this happening?"
I guess my richness of melanin is attracting grins
or the novelty of me is distracting her and him
I didn't take their invasion
as an attack from them
at first I wanted to protest
but anyhow I say "Ni hao" smile and nod saying "yes"
the woman comes over her 32 or less teeth
hanging out of her mouth with joyful glee
the man points and shoots
freezing that moment
that will become a story they share
they own it
they walk away smiling but I say "hey, come back"
I want to add to this like adlibs on a track
I communicate using google translate
I tell them who I am where I'm from and that they're great
I hopefully go from being a novelty
to a human being that they're seeing
being understood is freeing
although I'm not depending on them

giving that feeling
and with that they disappear
while I sit at the pier
peering into the future
already here

Before I travelled to China, I heard about other people's experiences. In fact I saw some YouTube videos of people getting stopped randomly on the street and asked to be in photographs. People told me that Chinese people are fascinated with black people. In my mind I braced myself for this to happen. It didn't happen like I thought it would.

In Shanghai I had this random woman and her son try to take a pic with me but I politely turned down the offer. However, when I was in Qingdao, this couple as I describe in the above verse tried to take a picture of me without me knowing. I was just sitting by the seafront and from the corner of my eye I could see them try to sneak a shot. Everything in the above poem happened as I wrote it.

Another time I was trying to take a photo of the sunset in Qingdao on the same day. I suddenly found myself surrounded by 3 middle-aged Chinese men. They were trying to see what I was doing on my phone. I used Google translate to communicate with them and they looked at each other, smiled, said some words in Chinese and walked away smiling at me.

I enjoyed my time out there. It was calm. One time I travelled on a train from one city to another and my luggage was checked. That was a thing different from London. You had x-ray machines checking your bags at train stations, even underground train stations every single time you used the train. My toothpaste was taken from my bag and a picture was taken of my passport. I found that puzzling and slightly amusing.

One last thing, I left China to come back to London 3 days before the first case of COVID-19 was discovered in Wuhan. I wasn't anywhere near that city, I was miles away in Qingdao but I found out the first case was discovered on November 17th 2019 and I left on November 13th.

Corona (Crown)

Greetings but no handshakes no hi fives
no hugs just foot taps elbow touches that's right
I don't trust no one to wash their hands
please understand don't come close just stand
a few feet away while I address you
please sneeze in the other direction bless you
that cough sounds rough man are you okay
enough is enough now be on your way
it's spreading as fast as misinformation
it's like they are racing on this occasion
it's hard to say who's in the lead
it depends on what you read and who you believe
if you see through a lens of doom and gloom
of course to you it seems the end is coming soon
oooh another conspiracy theory
with no evidence is clearly
spreading at the speed of fear
accelerating at the speed of panic
It's overtaking all reason here
and with quickness makes people frantic
but I understand 'cause nobody wants to die
but it doesn't help if we're also spreading lies
get information the right information
then get in formation this info war is tight

I was supposed to be in Romania
then Tanzania Sudan and Ethiopia
but all that cancelled and shut down for now
now I am sitting here and asking what now?
I'm washing my hands down every hour
limiting my news intake it disempowers

but I've got to stay informed
although second by second stats shouldn't be norm
I mean this is not a game this is not sport
and I don't want fear ruling my thoughts
I do not want fear to rule my emotions
I want to think clearly in the midst of this commotion
hand sanitizer, pasta, toilet roll
are sold out in the stores it's out of control
people are stockpiling it is wild man
I saw a viral vid of people getting violent
fighting in supermarkets over tissue paper
it's senseless do they think it is a lifesaver
but when fear hits ya it distorts the picture
it carries souls away when it flows like a river
but I understand 'cause nobody wants to die
but it doesn't help if we're also spreading lies
get information the right information
then get in formation this info war is tight

Just because something is plausible and possible
doesn't mean it's actual and factual
we all want answers that is natural
but where's your evidence
are facts backing you?
if you feel my words are attacking you
maybe deep down you know your words are lacking truth
many conspiracies are lacking proof
your shallow research is drowning you

This new collection was meant to be out in early 2020 but the pandemic hit the world and changed everything. I wrote these couple of verses a few days before the first lockdown in the UK. I recorded it as an actual song which I released on the day I had my last outing to visit a school. It is on my YouTube channel: KarlNova.

At the time so much misinformation was spreading so I wrote this because I was frustrated with how much unverified information was being spread as if they were facts. At a time like this, having accurate information is so important so that you can make crucial decisions. I saw people say that COVID-19 was a hoax and I was baffled by that when it was clear that it was a real thing.

COVID-19 is a coronavirus and coronaviruses have a crown-like appearance when seen under a microscope. Corona is the Latin word for "crown" and what I was trying to say with the song was that I won't let fear rule my mind and heart even though the situation of the world going through a pandemic was scary.

I was also saying we shouldn't let fear push us to spread false information and make up false stories to try to explain what was happening. What we need are facts so that we can take the right steps to get through this.

Wash Your Hands!

I went to the cinema and grabbed some popcorn
also a hotdog I won't say what I watched
the movie ended, it left me buzzing
the end credits rolled
I thought it was over
it wasn't
there was an extra scene that appeared on the screen
that made the eyes of the few of us who stayed gleam
I was glad I had dodged spoilers that could've spoiled it
I left the theatre but needed to use the toilet
I had to join a queue and wait to use the loo
I was only gonna do number one not number two
I did what I had to do then washed my hands
switched on the dryer to my left I saw this man
who came out of a cubicle he must've done a deuce
now understand this place wasn't busy or full
he was well dressed with his shirt, tie and suit
he didn't wash his hands he just left the room
I'm thinking what if he's a businessman heading for a meeting?
and someone offered their hand so glad to meet him
whoever that person was would never understand
how one looking respectable didn't wash his hands!

**This was written before the pandemic. Washing your hands and being
hygienic should be normal but it is amazing how unhygienic people
are. The importance of washing our hands in this time has been
highlighted even more.**

**I have become even more conscious of how germs spread because
of physical contact. I wouldn't consider myself to be a germophobe.**

I don't think I thought too deep about all of this before now. Seeing this well-dressed man walk in and walk out just like that without washing his hands really got me thinking. I wonder how many people do that daily? That is nasty!

I saw a video of some men greeting each other by touching their feet, I think that is a better option! I have also started doing elbow taps with people. I think this might be the way forward haha! I think handshakes are out for now!

When you see me, tap feet with me, or give me an elbow tap or at the very least a little bow will be accepted. You can give me a slight nod of the head to say hi as well. Bye handshakes! You are through for now!

In These Peculiar Times

Unprecedented is now an understatement
on my nerves that sentiment grinds
but how else can one describe?
these peculiar times

Like a punch to the face I can't dodge
like thoughts that haunt our minds
like a bad show we're forced to watch
are these peculiar times

Like a song with several key changes
carried by a heart that whines
you can't help but join in the chorus
in these peculiar times

So many badly drawn conclusions
responding to those othered drawing lines
I draw breath deeply and sigh
in these peculiar times

distorted narratives
and twisted headlines
what a time to be alive and online
in these peculiar times

being forged in the fires of history
the ongoing saga of humankind
we're just part of this confusing chapter
In these peculiar times

When the world asks who are you?
what will be your reply?
Mine is to ask "who are you too?"
in these peculiar times

A word I heard used a lot during this time especially is the word "unprecedented" and it means according to the Cambridge dictionary, "never having happened or existed before"

A pandemic breaking out exactly like this definitely has never happened in my life time. I've never had to experience a lockdown for example or wear a mask to get on the train. There have been pandemics before in history like the Spanish flu pandemic that happened from 1918 – 1920. It's funny it is called the Spanish flu because it was first discovered in Kansas, New York City and Camp Greene, North Carolina.

I was thinking a lot about the word unprecedented when I started writing this above poem. These are just thoughts I was putting down as I was living through this very peculiar time. I guess I was trying to make sense of everything.

There were times I looked out the window and my whole area was calm and quiet and I would say to myself "Is this really happening?". What a time to be alive.

Escape Route

I'm indoors
sitting on the floor, bored
acutely aware of squeaking floorboards
above me I wonder what's going on
as the fridge freezer whirs and purrs

Deep in thought
In this moment caught
I want to escape but the world's on pause
in my mind I rewind memories then fast forward
this will never feel normal it's awkward

I'm the sort
to turn things over and over
and turn 'em inside and out, I'm not closer
to cooking up a plot, in my mind's steaming pot
my Shawshank redemption is so far off

Time is short
so they say but it feels lengthened
we're sitting here as if it's detention
a lot of tension is whispered from the walls
"books are doors, get out now, don't stall!"

Shawshank Redemption is one of my favourite films. I am convinced it is one of the best films ever. I won't spoil it for you in case you haven't seen it but it involves escaping from prison.

As the lockdown went on, I longed more and more for a return to normal. I wrote a lot and tried to keep myself occupied. The whole world felt like it was put in detention. I wrote this thinking about that.

When I was in Lagos, I remember feeling trapped there. I felt like my life couldn't move forward unless I got out. I guess that is what a lot of people are feeling even as I write this. It will be interesting to look back on this when this pandemic is over.

I came across a very beautiful quote from Mason Cooley that says, "reading gives us someplace to go when we have to stay where we are". I have to say that is so true in any situation especially a lockdown. I read a lot! Reading is a way for your mind to escape. Your imagination can make you travel far away from where you are. Books are doors! Get out now! Don't stall!

If you are reading this in the future, this is how we felt and we hope something like this never happens again. History does tend to repeat itself though.

Boredom

Have you ever been so bored
a minute feels like an hour
and an hour feels like a day
boredom seems to tower
over your lack of interest
it's daunting when time drags
and your mind lags behind and wanders while time wags
its finger at you,
well it seems like it does
It seems like it mocks you and tells you off
for the way it drips slowly
watch it splash
drip
drip
drip
driving you mad
your mind is like a tap you can switch it off
you've got to learn what switches it on, it's tough
but you know what? Sometimes it's not
as you live you find out the things that you love
to be fed is what your imagination wants
boredom is hunger pains
when your mind needs to munch
So the next time you're bored
know it's time to eat
and make sure it's not just snacks
on which you feed

I really do believe boredom is simply your imagination wanting to be fed with something. We all get hungry. We all know what it's like when we eat and feel satisfied. We also all know what it's like to be fully engaged doing something we like.

I hardly get bored these days. There's so much to do and keep my mind occupied. There are things that get me bored. You know what does that for me? Long meetings. I mean I know sometimes meetings are needed to get some things going, it is what it is. When I'm bored and I can't do anything about it, I start writing rhymes in my head or I really try to focus on the present moment and observe everything around me.

One of the things we all have to learn to do is to be fully engaged in the present. It is not always an easy thing to do but it is very needed. At other times it is ok to let your imagination wander. It is ok to daydream.

To be fed is what your imagination wants...

New Normal?

First time on a train in 5 months
lockdown eased
it feels different
I stepped out of my ends to begin moving around
in a different world
we all have masks on except some of us
maybe their rebellion is a defence against
this "new normal"
a denial of that which has been
grimly snatching
a lot us away
people we all knew
that we now achingly miss
others had their masks
pulled down to below their chins
I saw a couple of people
with their masks on
but nose exposed
I tried not to accusingly stare
I used the cash point
before tapping my Oyster card
to go underground
I used hand sanitiser to eliminate
any possible sneaky germs
my headphones are on
music was my mask long before this time
a colourful one at that
like the one I have on my face presently
riding the tube is giving me
Shanghai memories

> their trains are cleaner there though
> I try not to touch anything
> except my phone that I clutch
> while typing out these thoughts

I wrote this while using the train for the first time in 5 months. It is one of the rare times I didn't rhyme. I have other verses I've written that way. I didn't include them in this collection.

I didn't leave my area during that first UK lockdown of 2020. I only left my house to go to the shop and go jogging almost every single day. I really kept to the rules.

It felt weird being on the train after so long with everything that had been happening. Everything I described was what I saw. My journey was to the music studio because I missed being there. I went to record songs that became part of a music project I released. It was called "Who Are You Too?" because it was sequel to an EP I released when I flew out to China.

The whole world felt different.

You Are Not Alone

I kick knowledge
with punchlines jab your mind
I'll slap box you awake it's not snooze time
this is crunch time
I'll tell you more than one time
times are serious though I have a fun time
Time whizzes by Wisdom whispers "hi!"
she says, "my guy please open up your eyes"
Information was talking fast to my right
Peace was peacefully sitting giving calm vibes
I see Understanding standing on the corner
Wisdom walks me to him I walk taller
Love sneaks up gives me a warm hug
Joy smiled at me and said to me "what's up?"
and then I noticed Patience standing right there
I was distracted by Fear's cold stare
he was standing in the shadows I felt cold air
but Wisdom and Understanding were still here

This is a verse that became part of a song called "Glide Through" that I recorded. It is on the "Who Are You Too?" mixtape project I released during the pandemic.

This is one of my favourite verses I've written. All the different good virtues in this verse are things I hope I communicate always. I know it starts off kind of strong and I think that just represents how tough I am on myself sometimes.

When I think I am being lazy or not doing what I know I should do, I find myself talking to myself and telling myself "What are you doing?!" I am sure I am not alone in this.

One of the beautiful things about poetry and literature in general is it helps you feel less alone. You find out you are not the only one that is experiencing whatever it is you are going through. You are definitely not alone.

Beautiful Ambition

Listen!
I'm not just daydreaming and wishing
I'm bursting with ambition
thirsting I drank wisdom
poured out in nan's kitchen
she fed me hope
and that expands vision
I saw many possibilities
I planned, thinking
I thought so big
I saw the future winking
showing me what is possible
my eyes glistened
inside belief has risen
though I have fallen due to hard collisions
hard collisions with obstacles
made my goals seem so impossible
those who can't see themselves shining
talk less of you
will likely be mocking you
but if they make fun of you
Just keep running through
the field of dreams
see them coming true
take steps as ambition burns in your chest
Work hard and be prepared for what's next

Hold on
Press on
Be strong

Filled with beautiful ambition

I got a phone call one day and found out the Premier League wanted me to write a poem for their premier league writing stars competition that they do. They wanted to use it to promote the competition. Not only that, they wanted me to come to their headquarters to video record me performing it. I never saw this coming!

I wrote something immediately after I finished the call because they needed it to be done in a short timeframe. The first version I wrote had lots of football metaphors because I thought "this is the premier league!" When I sent it to them I had already memorised that version but they said they needed something without all the football metaphors so I rewrote it and it became the finished verse above.

I memorised it and went to the Premier League office in Paddington to record it. I had rehearsed and rehearsed to get it right. I only had a day to prepare. It went well! I got to see the Premier League trophy up close and the fan in me jumped out! I wasn't allowed to touch it but I came closer to it than my favourite team Arsenal had in years!

I got to judge the competition with Wes Morgan captain of Leicester City and Cressida Cowell who is an amazing author later on. We had to meet via zoom virtually to choose the winner. If not for the pandemic we would have met to do it in person.

While I was at the Premier League office, I offhandedly said it would be nice if I could go back to my first school ever in Haverhill to do a presentation with the trophy and promote the competition and they actually said yes! This led me to going back to...

Burton End

Burton End was the beginning of these words
without it there would not even be a verse
for it was there in Haverhill that I first learnt
letters, sentences I'd use to mark the earth
even now I remember cursive writing homework
I was off school with the mumps I had to make those letters swirl
when I suddenly had to leave memories remained burnt
into mind as my life's pages turned
I always asked myself "would I ever get to return?"
and "would anyone even remember me?" my mind churned
I remember the slopes on the playground
In my head vivid images played around
I remembered doing pottery and drawing colourful art
It's strange how things have shaped up and those sparks
danced in my mind all this time
I returned like summertime sunshine, I survived!

When I asked the Premier League if I could go to Burton End with the Premier League trophy, I did it jokingly. I didn't fully expect them to make it happen but they did. There I was in my first school ever talking to students.

I looked around the school and could see things had obviously changed but some things were exactly the same like the slopes on the playground I had thought about since I was 7 and a half! I did a whole performance and some workshops as well. Then it was lunchtime and I went for a stroll.

I went to look for the house where Nan used to live. 21 Hazel Close is still there. The street and house looked like how I remembered it.

I didn't realise how close the school was to where I lived, I guess when you are a child everything seems much bigger and further than it actually is.

I stood there taking pictures and thought about Nan, Mrs V. Butterick. I knew she was long gone. No one had to tell me over the years that she had passed on. It was something I never asked my mother about, I just knew and accepted it.

I kept asking myself "How in the world did my mother find such a random out of town place like this to send me to?". Haverhill doesn't have its own train station! I had so many questions. I wondered if Nan had relatives that still lived in Haverhill. I wondered what happened to the boys who bullied me that I beat up one after the other? None of these questions were answered but being there meant a lot to me. It made me feel that all my memories I had stored in my mind all this time were not crazy thoughts of a past life.

I walked to the park close by that I could only vaguely remember. All I could think of is I have come a long way. I am not just talking about a long way to travel to Haverhill from London on that particular day but a long way in life to be able to be back in this particular way. I kept writing and scribbling my dreams through everything I have been through and because of rhythm and poetry I was back where I first learnt to write in the first place.

Future Memories

After all is said and done
all we'll have are memories
and one day a memory
is all you'll be
so before I turn to dust
and become a story
I'll store up my precious moments
and not forgetfully leave
or forgetfully live
I'll fill my memory bank
with rich deposits
it will never be blank
how could it be empty?
when so many glowing instances
show up on my path
these riches are infinite
I hold them carefully
and share with joy
doing that repeatedly
means they can't be destroyed
after all is said and done
all we'll have are memories
and one day a memory
is all you'll be

And so we end up here. Memories are precious things. I never took mine for granted because at some point all that kept me going were my precious memories. I decided to share some of them in this collection with you. Thank you for reading. I hope it touches you and inspires you even if it is in a small way. Our memories matter because we matter.

After writing my first book, I wasn't sure how I was going to approach putting this collection together. I felt like after all the attention my first book ever received that nothing I would write could match it. Then I realised it is so silly to think that way. I had so much more to share and as I moved around, I had to let it come naturally.

I hope these words of mine let you know you can make it through even the hardest times, never give up, never quit and even if you fall down, get back up. I hope it makes someone feel less alone. You can make it through. I don't share these stories in a sad way, they are for me shared with joy, I won, I survived, I am here. I lived to tell it.

The Rhythm And Poetry Anthem

Rhythm and poetry R-A-P
speak from the heart and be free
We are intelligent we are smart
We always finish what we start

You feed your mind when you read
We work hard we will succeed
We won't stop we won't give up
We will keep rising to the top

You have two ears and one mouth
Listen more than you speak out
Words have power this I know
I'll keep learning as I grow

Always listen to what's said
Lock those facts inside your head
Always care for your friends
Together there's nothing you can't mend

Love your family all the time
Keep your home in your mind
I hope your dreams do come true
You know everyone loves you

Always have faith in your heart
Be yourself and play your part
just be brave don't be scared
Make sure that you are prepared

Think of what you want to be
Look to the future you want to see
Don't let anyone hold you back
Do not get pushed off the track

I made a promise so that is why I am adding this as a bonus. I got to be the artist in residence at Tithe Farm School in Houghton Regis for over a year in 2018 and some days in 2019. I would go there every Friday and do creative writing sessions. I loved doing this because this was the first time I really got to spend time in a place for an extended period of time. It really stretched me as a creative practitioner, workshop facilitator and an artist.

Out of these sessions we created this long rap anthem. I made the whole school learn the whole thing. I told them that I would include it in this new collection. I hope they see this and are reading this. I want them to know I never forgot them. This is something I want everyone to learn. It has a very simple rhythm and it works when you say it loud together.

Acknowledgements

I'm thankful for the blessing and grace of being able to share in this way. This is something I will never take for granted. I'm thankful to everyone who will read this, understand it and share how it has touched them, moved them and hopefully made them feel seen and heard. I dedicate this to all those curious ones out there who are scribbling their dreams right now.

**Rhythm and Poetry by Karl Nova available from
trevor@caboodlebooks.co.uk price £5.99**